CONTENTS

Grammar Workshop

Level Green

Beverly Ann Chin, Ph.D.

Senior Series Consultant
Professor of English
University of Montana
Missoula, MT

Reviewers

The publisher wishes to thank the following teachers for their thorough review and thoughtful comments on portions of the series prior to publication.

Timothy Beaumont
Maplewood, New Jersey

Renea Boles
Flourtown, Pennsylvania

Stacy Donaghy
Little Rock, Arkansas

Christine Ganey
New York, New York

Maria James
San José, California

Stephanie Richardson
Compton, California

Nancy Wahl
New York, New York

Roseanne Williby
Omaha, Nebraska

Photo Credits

Alamy/David Fleetham: 188; Lana Sundman: 144; V&A Images: 170. Art Resource, NY: 20; The Art Archive/Culver Pictures: 38; The Kobal Collection/MGM: 102. www.banknotes.com: 49. The Bicycle Museum of America/New Bremen, OH: 17. Cass Photography/Lake Villa, Il/Alex and Paula Rothacker/Grayslake, IL: 13. Copyright DaimlerChrysler Corporation/Used with permission: 90. Corbis/Bettmann: 85, 174, 176, 218; Gallo Images/Martin Harvey: 140; Horace Bristol: 36; Joseph Sohm/Visions of America: 120; Lawrence Manning: 169; Paul A. Souders: 217; Reuters/Jim Bourg: 104. Courtesy of Laura Ingalls Wilder Home Association Mansfield, MO: 221. Getty Images/Blend Images/JGI/Jamie Grill: 225; Collection Mix/ Code Red: 101; Digital Vision/Paul Souders: 141; Getty Images Sport/NASA/Handout: 34; Image Source: 210; LOOK/ Harald Eisenberger: 16; Photodisc/Siede Preis: 26, 180; Photographic Choice RF/Andrew Holt: 127; Riser/Stephen Stickler: 18; Stocktrek Images: 32; Stone/Javier Pierini: 94; Taxi/David Sacks: 209 *top*; The Image Bank/Art Wolfe: 65. iStockphoto. com/Michael Krinke: 146; PhotoFritz: 145; Saga Photography: 216. Masterfile/Royalty Free: 96, 224. Mountain Light/ Galen Rowell: 128. Photo Copyright Laura Ingalls Wilder Memorial Society, De Smet, S.D.: 222. Punchstock/Blend Images: 172; Comstock: 83; Creatas Images: 130, 134; Digital Vision: 52, 61, 74, 166, 209 *bottom*; Photodisc: 12, 54, 98, 132; Photographer's Choise RF: 162. Used under permission from Shutterstock.com/Anette Linnea Rasmussen: 73; Carolyn Brule: 80; Elias H. Debbas II: 105; Feng Yu: 53; Ian Scott: 190; Ilya Genkin: 136; iofoto: 202; Jessica Bilen: 78; Joshua Haviv: 84; Kristian Sekulic: 133; Mihhail Tribol: 39; Nina Shannon: 108; Ralf Juergen Kraft: 168; Scott Maxwell: 30; .shock: 225; Studiotouch: 220. TheHenryFord.org: 177. U.S. Department of the Treasury/The United States Mint: 50; The U.S. National Archives and Records Administration: 48. The U.S. National Archives and Records Administration: 178.

Illustrators

Ron Berg: 112, 113, 114, 150, 160, 161, 164, 196, 198, 200. Ken Bowser: 15, 56, 57, 58, 72, 75, 109, 122, 138, 182. John Ceballos: 60, 62, 63, 81, 142. Mena Dolobowsky: 135. CD Hullinger: 22, 97, 206, 207. Nathan Jarvis: 28, 29, 88, 92, 100. Martin Lemelman: 8, 9, 10, 44, 45, 46, 76, 77, 79, 124, 125, 126, 156, 157, 159, 192, 194. Bob Masheris: 24, 25, 64, 66. Zina Saunders: 121. Paul Weiner: 173, 212, 214.

For additional online resources, go to grammarworkshop.com **and enter the Student Access Code: GW13SGGK8TZM**

ONLINE COMPONENTS
available for computer and tablet at
grammarworkshop.com

(See page ii for the student access code.)

• Interactive Quiz for Every Lesson

• Extra Practice for Every Lesson

• Proofreading Worksheets for Every Unit

NOTE TO STUDENTS

You already know how to read, speak, and write English. So why should you learn grammar?

What Is Grammar?

Like all languages, English has rules about how words can be put together in sentences. Learning these rules will help you to speak and write so that everyone understands you. When you study grammar, you learn that words in English can be grouped into different parts. These parts include nouns, verbs, adjectives, adverbs, and pronouns. Grammar tells you how to put these parts together correctly.

How Will Grammar Help You?

Knowing grammar will help you to become a better reader, speaker, and writer. Knowing how language works will help you to read with more understanding. It will help you to express your feelings and ideas clearly. Your writing will be easier to follow. You will also make fewer mistakes when you do homework and take tests.

What Is Grammar Workshop?

GRAMMAR WORKSHOP is designed to teach you the rules of English and to give you lots and lots of practice. This book is called a WORKSHOP because it teaches in ways that make you work. You don't just read and memorize. You have to Learn, Practice, and Write.

Ready, Set, Go Grammar!

Now it's time to get started. Have fun, learn those rules—and go grammar!

Lesson 1: **Sentences**

LEARN

A **sentence** is a group of words that expresses a complete thought.

A sentence usually tells *who* or *what* does something.
It also tells *what happens* or *what is done*.

A **fragment** is a group of words that does not express
a complete thought.

Fragment	**Sentence**
Told stories long ago.	Aesop told stories long ago.
Called the stories fables.	He called the stories fables.
The fables.	The fables teach lessons.

Every sentence begins with a capital letter.

PRACTICE

A *Read each group of words. Circle **sentence** if it expresses a complete thought. Circle **fragment** if it does not.*

1. Tortoise and Hare had a race.   *sentence*   *fragment*

2. A very fast hare.   *sentence*   *fragment*

3. Tortoise moved along slowly.   *sentence*   *fragment*

4. Hare raced out in front.   *sentence*   *fragment*

5. Would beat Tortoise easily.   *sentence*   *fragment*

6. Took a little nap along the way.   *sentence*   *fragment*

7. Tortoise never stopped.   *sentence*   *fragment*

8. Tortoise passed the sleeping hare.   *sentence*   *fragment*

9. Crossed the finish line first.   *sentence*   *fragment*

10. A surprise winner.   *sentence*   *fragment*

B *Each group of words in Column A and each group of words in Column B is a fragment. Match a group of words in Column A with a group of words in Column B to form a sentence. Write the letter of the words you choose on the line. Your sentences should tell a story. The first one is done for you.*

A	B
_c_ **1.** A shepherd boy	**a.** pretended to see a wolf.
____ **2.** The hours	**b.** rushed out to chase the wolf.
____ **3.** Some excitement	**c.** watched his sheep in a field.
____ **4.** The boy	**d.** passed very slowly.
____ **5.** All the people from town	**e.** would make the day interesting.

A	B
____ **6.** The people	**f.** scolded the boy for his silly trick.
____ **7.** They	**g.** really did attack the sheep the next day.
____ **8.** A wolf	**h.** were heard in the town again.
____ **9.** The boy's shouts	**i.** came to help this time.
____ **10.** No one	**j.** found no wolf in the field.

C *Make each fragment a complete sentence by adding a group of words from the box. The first one is done for you.*

> could not reach the water   saw a pitcher of water on a table
> was in the pitcher   the situation
> the big bird

1. A very thirsty crow _____ *saw a pitcher of water on a table* _____ .

2. Only a little water _____ .

3. _____ put his beak into the pitcher.

4. His beak _____ .

5. _____ seemed hopeless.

> dropped a pebble into the pitcher
> suddenly came to the crow
> enjoyed a nice drink
> quickly followed
> the level of the water

6. A bright idea _____ .

7. He _____ .

8. More pebbles _____ .

9. _____ rose slowly to the top of the pitcher.

10. Then the clever crow _____ .

Revising Sentences

WRITE

D *Add a group of words to each fragment to make a complete sentence. Write the sentence on the line. Remember to capitalize the first word in the sentence.*

1. loves to read fables _____

_____

2. A very hungry fox _____

_____

3. worked hard all summer _____

_____

4. The lion's paw _____

_____

5. played a trick on the donkey _____

_____

6. chased the cat into a tree _____

_____

7. A silly old goose _____

_____

8. could not swim in the water _____

_____

9. walked away from the gold _____

_____

10. The wise old woman _____

_____

Lesson 2: Statements and Questions

LEARN

Statements and questions are two kinds of sentences.

- A **statement** tells something.
  A statement ends with a period (.).

  I like to read about animals.
  Some facts about animals are amazing.

- A **question** asks something.
  A question ends with a question mark (**?**).

  Which animals do you like?
  Have you ever seen a bald eagle?

Every sentence begins with a capital letter.

PRACTICE

A *Circle the words that describe each sentence. If the sentence tells something, write **statement**. If the sentence asks something, write **question**. The first one is done for you.*

1. The bald eagle is our national bird.
(tells something)   *statement*
asks something

2. It is often listed in record books.
tells something   _____
asks something

3. Can you guess why?
tells something   _____
asks something

4. Is it the world's largest bird?
tells something   _____
asks something

5. Does it lay the most eggs?
tells something   _____
asks something

6. The bald eagle builds the largest nest. *tells something* _____
asks something

7. The nest can be eight feet wide. *tells something* _____
asks something

8. The nest can weigh up to 4000 pounds. *tells something* _____
asks something

9. There's just one thing I'd like to know. *tells something* _____
asks something

10. How does the nest stay in a tree? *tells something* _____
asks something

B Add a period (.) to end each statement. Add a question mark (?)
to end each question.

1. Have you ever heard of Olive Oyl ____

2. Olive Oyl is the name of a cartoon character ____

3. Olive Oyl is also the name of a dog ____

4. She belongs to a police dog trainer ____

5. What makes Olive Oyl special ____

6. She has a special talent ____

7. Olive Oyl likes to jump rope with
her family ____

8. Her record is 63 jumps a minute ____

9. Can you break Olive Oyl's record ____

10. Do you know a dog that jumps faster ____

Olive Oyl jumping rope

C *Here is a list of questions and answers about koalas. It has four missing capital letters and four incorrect end marks. Look for the mistakes, and fix them. Use the proofreading marks in the box.*

Frequently Asked Questions About Koalas

Q: Are koalas bears.

A: Koalas are not bears. They look just like teddy bears. they are related to kangaroos.

Q: Where can you find koalas.

A: Koalas live in Australia. you can find them in certain trees.

Q: what do koalas do during the day?

A: Koalas sleep all day.

Q: What do koalas do at night?

A: Koalas move around and eat at night?

Q: What do koalas eat?

A: koalas eat leaves from trees.

Q: Which animal record does the koala hold?

A: The koala is the world's sleepiest animal? It sleeps from 18 to 20 hours each day.

Proofreading Marks

∧	Add
⊙	Period
℘	Take out
≡	Capital letter
/	Small letter

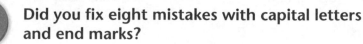

Did you fix eight mistakes with capital letters and end marks?

WRITE

D Write a statement and a question about each animal below. In your statement, write what you know about the animal. In your question, write what you would like to ask about the animal.

1. Statement _____

_____

Question _____

_____

2. Statement _____

_____

Question _____

_____

3. Statement _____

_____

Question _____

_____

Proofreading Checklist ✓

❑ Does each statement and question begin with a
capital letter?
❑ Does each statement end with a period?
❑ Does each question end with a question mark?

Lesson 3: Commands and Exclamations

LEARN

Commands and exclamations are also kinds of sentences.

- A **command** tells someone to do something. A command ends with a period.

  Get your bicycle.
  Please follow bike safety rules.

- An **exclamation** shows strong feeling. An exclamation ends with an exclamation mark (**!**).

  What a great bike trail we're on!
  Wow, I won the bike race!
  I just got a flat tire!

Every sentence begins with a capital letter.

PRACTICE

A *Read each sentence. Circle **command** if the sentence tells someone to do something. Circle **exclamation** if the sentence shows strong feeling.*

1. Make sure your bike helmet fits properly.   *command*   *exclamation*

2. Ride on the right-hand side of the trail.   *command*   *exclamation*

3. What a busy street this is!   *command*   *exclamation*

4. Please walk your bike across the street.   *command*   *exclamation*

5. Always pass other bikers on the left.   *command*   *exclamation*

6. Watch for people crossing the road.   *command*   *exclamation*

7. I can't believe how fast you're pedaling!   *command*   *exclamation*

8. Oh, your front tire needs air!   *command*   *exclamation*

9. Stop and fill it right away.   *command*   *exclamation*

10. That was a really great ride!   *command*   *exclamation*

B *Add a period (.) to end each command. Add an exclamation mark (!) to end each exclamation. The clue in ( ) will help you.*

1. Please come with us to the Bicycle Museum of America ____ (command)

2. What an amazing collection of old bicycles we'll see ____ (exclamation)

3. Take a look at this bicycle from 1870 ____ (command)

4. Wow, the wheels are made of wood ____ (exclamation)

5. That's amazing ____ (exclamation)

6. Read the label on this bicycle ____ (command)

7. Hey, it was nicknamed the "Boneshaker" ____ (exclamation)

8. What a bumpy ride you would have on it ____ (exclamation)

9. Look at the Columbia Expert bicycle from 1883 ____ (command)

10. Notice the huge front wheels on these old bikes ____ (command)

11. Wow, they must be five feet high ____ (exclamation)

12. I can't believe how bicycles have changed ____ (exclamation)

Boneshaker

C Read this poster about a town's yearly bicycle day. Find the four missing capital letters and the four missing end marks in the sentences. Use the proofreading marks to fix the mistakes.

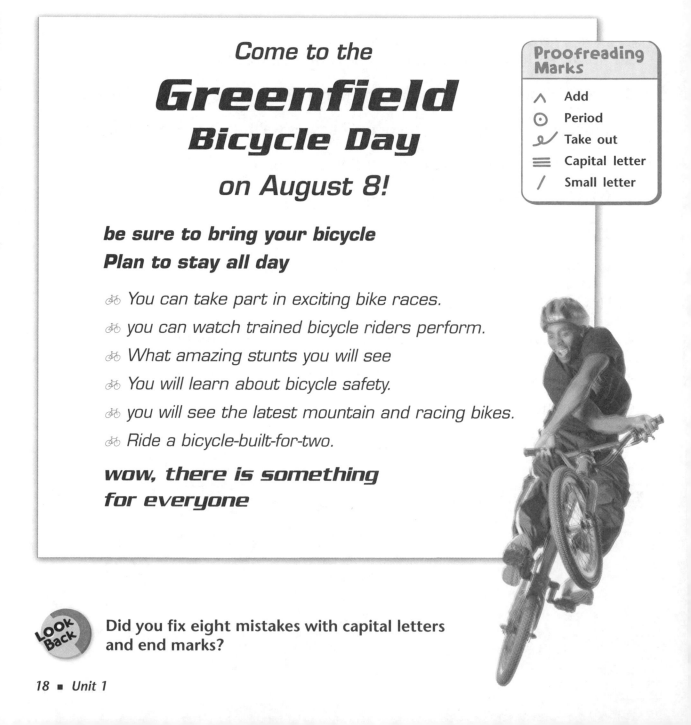

Come to the

Greenfield
Bicycle Day
on August 8!

Proofreading Marks

∧	Add
⊙	Period
ℓ	Take out
≡	Capital letter
/	Small letter

be sure to bring your bicycle
Plan to stay all day

🚲 You can take part in exciting bike races.

🚲 you can watch trained bicycle riders perform.

🚲 What amazing stunts you will see

🚲 You will learn about bicycle safety.

🚲 you will see the latest mountain and racing bikes.

🚲 Ride a bicycle-built-for-two.

wow, there is something for everyone

Look Back Did you fix eight mistakes with capital letters and end marks?

Additional Resources at
grammarworkshop.com

Write Your Own

WRITE

D *Imagine you are in each situation below. Write a command or an exclamation that you might say in each situation. The first one is done for you.*

1. Some people are walking ahead of you on a bike trail. They don't hear you riding up behind them.

You say _Look out for the bicycle!_____

2. You are biking with some friends. One friend isn't wearing a helmet.

You say _____

3. You hit a home run during a softball game.

You say _____

4. You want your parents to watch you swim across the pool.

You say _____

5. You want your friends to be quiet for the opening song before a ball game.

You say _____

6. You are afraid you are going to be late for the soccer game.

You say _____

7. You want your friends to meet you at a certain time to go biking.

You say _____

8. You and your friends reach the top of a high hill after a long hike.

You say _____

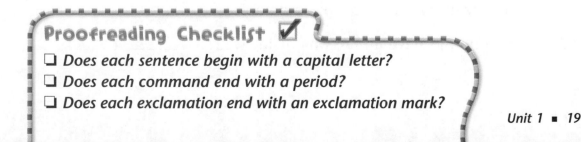

Proofreading Checklist ✓

❑ *Does each sentence begin with a capital letter?*
❑ *Does each command end with a period?*
❑ *Does each exclamation end with an exclamation mark?*

Lesson 4: **Simple Sentences: Subjects**

LEARN

A **simple sentence** expresses a complete thought. It has two parts. The **subject** is the part that tells *whom* or *what* the sentence is about. The subject can be one word or more than one word.

> **Murals** are paintings on walls.
> **Many famous artists** have painted murals.
> **Our class** is painting a mural, too!

The subject usually comes at the beginning of a sentence.

PRACTICE

A *Read each sentence. Ask yourself whom or what the sentence is about. Then write the subject on the line.*

1. Many artists paint murals. _____

2. Some murals were painted long ago. _____

3. Hunters painted them inside caves. _____

4. These amazing drawings show animals. _____

5. The Romans liked murals, too. _____

6. Their wall paintings showed great heroes. _____

7. Our class has seen several murals. _____

8. City Hall has a colorful mural. _____

9. The library mural shows people and books. _____

10. Other buildings have murals on outside walls. _____

B *Circle the subject that best completes the sentence. Then write the subject on the line. The first one is done for you.*

1. _____Our schoolyard_____ has gray cement walls.

  (Our schoolyard)   The tall tree

2. _____ will add color to these walls.

  Murals   Books

3. _____ is planning a mural for the schoolyard.

  Each class   The last place

4. _____ vote on different ideas for the murals.

  Shoppers   Students

5. _____ is a popular choice.

  My uncle   Outer space

6. _____ also got many votes.

  The cost of paint   The idea of sports

7. _____ is the winning choice for my class.

  The rainforest   My homework

8. _____ will help the students on Saturday.

  Some parents   The murals

9. _____ are also helping the students.

  Two reasons   Local artists

10. _____ has given us paint and brushes.

  A store   A colorful painting

11. _____ will paint part of a mural.

  Another example   Every student

12. _____ will win a prize.

  The best mural   Only one color

C Write a subject to complete each sentence. Choose a subject from the box, or use a subject of your own.

Remember 💡
The **subject** tells *whom* or *what* the sentence is about.

> My class   Three dolphins   A boat   Our mural
> Our teacher   The local paper   Waves   Seagulls
> Puffy clouds   A lighthouse

1. _____ painted a sea mural.

2. _____ is eighteen feet long.

3. _____ float in the sky.

4. _____ leap out of the water.

5. _____ is on a distant shore.

6. _____ fly above the dolphins.

7. _____ have big curves.

8. _____ carries people across the sea.

9. _____ was proud of our finished mural.

10. _____ wrote a story about our mural!

Write Your Own

WRITE

D In the box, sketch a mural that you might paint someday. Then write four or more sentences to describe your mural. Underline the subject of each sentence you write. Check a dictionary if you need help spelling a word.

Proofreading Checklist ☑

❏ Does each sentence have a subject?
❏ Does each subject tell **whom** or **what** the sentence is about?

Lesson 5: Simple Sentences: Predicates

LEARN

A simple sentence has two parts. The subject is one part of a sentence. The other part is the predicate. The **predicate** tells what the subject *does* or *is*. The predicate can be one word or more than one word.

The seasons **change**.
The seasons **change four times a year**.
Each season **has its beauty**.

The predicate usually follows the subject of a sentence.

PRACTICE

A *Read each sentence. Ask yourself what the subject does or is to find the predicate. Then write the predicate on the line.*

1. Spring began on March 21. _____

2. The snow melted long ago. _____

3. Some April showers fall. _____

4. The days are longer and warmer. _____

5. Pretty tulips bloom in the spring. _____

6. The meadow grass is bright green. _____

7. Birds build nests in the trees. _____

8. Baseball teams play in the park. _____

9. My neighbors plant seeds in the garden. _____

10. The whole world feels brand new. _____

B *Match a subject in Column A with a predicate in Column B to form a sentence. Write the letter of the predicate you choose on the line. The first one is done for you.*

A	*B*
_e_ **1.** Summertime	**a.** keep us cool indoors.
____ **2.** Our school	**b.** wears shorts.
____ **3.** The town swimming pool	**c.** cook on the hot grill.
____ **4.** Fourth of July fireworks	**d.** light up the nighttime sky.
____ **5.** The temperature	**e.** begins in late June.
____ **6.** Everyone	**f.** might hit 100 degrees today!
____ **7.** Air conditioners	**g.** opens on July 1.
____ **8.** Hamburgers	**h.** marks the end of summer.
____ **9.** The beach	**i.** closes for over two months.
____ **10.** Labor Day	**j.** is fun on a hot day.

C Write a predicate to complete each sentence. Choose a predicate from the box, or use a predicate of your own.

> blow in the wind   practice on the field
> keep people warm   has a new teacher
> begins in late September grow huge in the fields
> begins in December   is delicious
> fly south   gather acorns

1. Autumn _____.

2. Fallen leaves _____.

3. My class _____.

4. Football players _____.

5. Wool sweaters _____.

6. The wild geese _____.

7. Pumpkins _____.

8. Squirrels _____.

9. Thanksgiving Day dinner _____.

10. Winter _____.

WRITE

D *Think about each month of winter. Write two sentences about something you might do in each month. Underline the predicate of each sentence you write. Check a dictionary if you need help spelling a word.*

December

_____

_____

_____

_____

January

_____

_____

_____

_____

February

_____

_____

_____

_____

Proofreading Checklist ☑

❏ *Does each sentence have a subject and a predicate?*
❏ *Does each sentence begin with a capital letter?*
❏ *Does each sentence end with an end mark?*

Lesson 6: **Compound Sentences**

LEARN

- Sometimes two simple sentences contain related ideas. The sentences can be joined to form a **compound sentence**. Joining sentences in this way will make your writing smoother and clearer. The word *and* or *but* can be used to join the sentences.

  RELATED SENTENCES
  My parents pick a movie. I like their choice.

  COMPOUND SENTENCE
  My parents pick a movie, **and** I like their choice.

  RELATED SENTENCES
  I like science fiction. My father prefers comedies.

  COMPOUND SENTENCE
  I like science fiction, **but** my father prefers comedies.

- The joining words *and* and *but* are called **coordinating conjunctions**. A comma (,) goes before *and* or *but* in a compound sentence.

PRACTICE

A *Read each sentence. Circle* **compound** *if it is made up of two related sentences with a joining word. Circle* **not a compound** *if it is not.*

1. I choose a theater, and Dad drives us there.   *compound   not a compound*

2. Twelve different movies are playing there.   *compound   not a compound*

3. Dad buys the tickets, and I get some popcorn.   *compound   not a compound*

4. Our movie starts at 2:20, but we arrive early.   *compound   not a compound*

5. We choose the best seats in the empty theater.   *compound   not a compound*

6. I like to sit near the screen, but Dad doesn't.   *compound   not a compound*

7. More and more people slowly enter the theater.   *compound   not a compound*

8. The lights dim, and the audience quiets down.   *compound*   *not a compound*

9. The coming attractions always look exciting.   *compound*   *not a compound*

10. Our movie begins to play at last.   *compound*   *not a compound*

B *Underline the two related sentences in each compound sentence.
Circle the coordinating conjunction that joins them. If the sentence
is not a compound sentence, write **not a compound**.*

1. A spaceship lands on Earth, and space creatures get out.

_____

2. The creatures are scary-looking, but I'm not afraid
of them.

_____

3. The movie starts off slowly, but it gets really exciting.

_____

4. The main character is a young scientist named Mark.

_____

5. He tries to warn people about the space creatures.

_____

6. The movie has an exciting ending, but I won't give it away.

_____

7. I loved the movie, and I want to see it again.

_____

8. The movie just opened this week, and I think it will run a long time.

_____

C *This is Anna's report about early movies. Find the six mistakes in the compound sentences, and fix them. Use the proofreading marks in the box.*

Remember 💡
The word *and* or *but* can join two sentences to form a **compound sentence**. A comma (,) goes before the joining word.

The first movie was shown in 1895. Early movies were very simple but people still liked them. One movie just showed a waterfall, And another showed a crowd of people in a street.

People at first thought movies were real. One early movie showed the ocean and people in the theater jumped out of the way. They thought they would get wet!

Proofreading Marks

∧	Add
⊙	Period
ℓ	Take out
≡	Capital letter
/	Small letter

Early movie theaters were empty stores with rows of chairs. They were called nickelodeons and they charged five cents. The movies had no sound, But a piano player played music.

The Great Train Robbery was a 1903 movie. This film was only 11 minutes long but it was an important movie. It was the first movie to tell a story!

Did you fix six mistakes in the compound sentences?

WRITE

D *Each pair of sentences below tells about a famous movie. Combine the sentences to form a compound sentence. Use the word in ( ) to join them. Remember to put a comma before the joining word. The first one is done for you.*

1. The movie *Pinocchio* was made in 1940. It is still popular today. (but)

The movie Pinocchio was made in 1940, but it is still popular today.

2. Pinocchio is a puppet. He wants to be a little boy. (but)

3. Jiminy Cricket is a wise friend. He gives Pinocchio good advice. (and)

4. Pinocchio won't listen to Jiminy. He gets into a lot of trouble. (and)

5. A whale chases the puppet. The puppet almost turns into a donkey. (and)

6. Pinocchio becomes brave and kind. The movie has a happy ending. (and)

Lesson 7: Complex Sentences

LEARN

- You have learned that a compound sentence is formed by joining two related ideas with the words *and* or *but*.

- A **complex sentence** also has two related ideas. The related ideas are joined by a **subordinating conjunction**.

  Look at the sentence below. The two related ideas are underlined. The subordinating conjunction **after** joins the two related ideas.

  I became interested in the moon **after** I saw a show about the U.S. space program.

  The following subordinating conjunctions are often used to connect related ideas.

Subordinating Conjunctions		
after	although	because
before	until	when

- The subordinating conjunction may come at the beginning of the sentence.

  Because they were so far away, I used a telescope to look at the stars.

Notice that when the first idea in the sentence begins with a subordinating conjunction, a comma follows that idea.

PRACTICE

A *Read each sentence. Circle **complex** if the sentence is made up of two related ideas joined by a subordinating conjunction. Circle **not complex** if it is not a complex sentence.*

1. Sometimes, we can see the moon during the day.   *complex*   *not complex*

2. The moon looks bright because light from the sun bounces off it.   *complex*   *not complex*

3. It is easier to see the moon after the sun sets.   *complex*   *not complex*

4. The moon circles Earth in about twenty-seven days.   *complex*   *not complex*

5. We see the different phases of the moon when it circles Earth.   *complex*   *not complex*

6. Scientists knew little about the moon's surface until they sent landers there.   *complex*   *not complex*

7. Scientists did not want the landers to sink into the moon's dusty surface.   *complex*   *not complex*

8. Twelve astronauts walked on the moon between 1969 and 1972.   *complex*   *not complex*

9. Before the astronauts returned to Earth, they gathered samples of moon rocks and soil.   *complex*   *not complex*

B *Read each complex sentence. Underline the subordinating conjunction that joins the two related ideas. Then write it on the line.*

1. Although scientists have traveled to the moon, none have set foot on Mars yet.   _____

2. It may be many years before they land on the planet.   _____

3. Humans cannot visit Mars until they can protect themselves from the sun's harmful rays.   _____

4. Scientists became even more excited about exploring Mars when they made a new discovery.   _____

5. They think that the rivers and lakes on Mars disappeared after its atmosphere changed.   _____

6. Mars is often called the red planet because it is covered with red dirt and rocks.   _____

C *Choose a subordinating conjunction from the box to complete each sentence. Write it on the line.*

Remember

A **complex sentence** is formed by joining two related ideas with a subordinating conjunction.

after   although   because

before   until   when

1. I went to space camp _____ I wanted to learn more about space exploration.

2. _____ I learned about Mars, I decided to become an astronaut.

3. _____ NASA seeks new astronauts, it looks for people who have studied math and science.

4. _____ you can become an astronaut, you must train long and hard.

5. Training begins _____ you have learned about aircraft safety.

6. _____ you can become an astronaut, you must be comfortable living and working with others in small spaces.

7. _____ training and spaceflights can be demanding, astronauts must be in good health.

8. Scientists cannot go on space missions _____ they can perform tasks where there is no gravity.

9. Learning another language is helpful _____ astronauts must work with scientists from all over the world.

10. _____ not every scientist becomes an astronaut, some work for NASA in other ways.

WRITE

D Write a complex sentence by adding a related idea either before
or after each item. Write the sentence on the line. Remember to put
a comma after the first idea if the sentence starts with a subordinating
conjunction. You can use a dictionary to help you spell words.

1. because the planets are far away _____

_____

2. after the sun sets _____

_____

3. until we see the full moon _____

_____

4. although it looks as if there are lakes on the moon _____

_____

5. because there is no gravity in space _____

_____

When someone you are speaking to asks you a question,
you might answer using a sentence fragment that starts with
a subordinating conjunction.

   "Why are you so excited about space?"
   "Because I just saw a great television show about it!"

When you write a report or complete a school assignment,
however, you should use complete sentences.

Proofreading Checklist ✓

❏ *Does each sentence have correct capitalization?*
❏ *Are words spelled correctly?*
❏ *Does each complex sentence have a subordinating
   conjunction that joins the two ideas?*

Lesson 8: Run-on Sentences

LEARN

A **run-on sentence** is two complete sentences that run together.

> **INCORRECT**   Kites are fun to fly people all over the world fly them.

- **You can correct a run-on sentence by writing it as two sentences. Use an end mark after the first sentence. Begin the second sentence with a capital letter.**

> **CORRECT**   Kites are fun to fly. People all over the world fly them.

- **You can often correct a run-on sentence by rewriting it as a compound sentence.**

> **CORRECT**   Kites are fun to fly, **and** people all over the world fly them.

PRACTICE

A *Read each group of words. Circle* **correct** *if it is a correctly written sentence. Circle* **run-on** *if it is a run-on sentence.*

1. The Japanese have flown kites for 1400 years their kites are famous.   *correct*   *run-on*

2. Kites are more than a fun sport in Japan they are works of art.   *correct*   *run-on*

3. Artists paint the kites their paintings have special meaning.   *correct*   *run-on*

4. A kite might show a great hero.   *correct*   *run-on*

5. Some kites are shaped like birds, but others are shaped like dragons or fish.   *correct*   *run-on*

6. Japanese kites come in all sizes, and many are quite large.   *correct*   *run-on*

7. One kite was 60 feet wide its tail was 480 feet long.   *correct*   *run-on*

8. Another kite weighed 2 tons.   *correct*   *run-on*

9. Kite festivals are popular in Japan thousands of people take part.   *correct*   *run-on*

10. Each neighborhood builds a kite then the neighborhoods compete against each other.   *correct*   *run-on*

 B *Write each run-on sentence correctly. Use **and** or **but** if you choose to rewrite the run-on as a compound sentence.*

1. A glider is a plane without an engine the moving air keeps it up.

_____

_____

2. An airplane pulls a glider into the sky then the plane lets go of the glider.

_____

_____

3. Gliders have thin bodies and wings these bodies and wings can catch airflows.

_____

_____

4. Glider flights can last for hours there is time to enjoy the view.

_____

_____

5. A hang glider looks like a big kite it is a special kind of glider.

_____

_____

C *This is John's report about the first airplane flight. Look for the seven run-on sentences, and fix them. Use the proofreading marks in the box.*

First to Fly

Orville and Wilbur Wright wanted to fly. They built kites they flew gliders. They also read books about flight.

The two brothers built the *Flyer* in 1903. It was the world's first airplane with a motor the Wrights even built the motor themselves.

The *Flyer*'s wings were 40 feet long the plane weighed 750 pounds. It cost less than $1000 to build.

Orville and Wilbur went to Kitty Hawk in North Carolina for their first flight. Everything was ready Orville took off first. The *Flyer* lifted 10 feet into the air. The flight lasted 12 seconds it covered 120 feet.

The Wright brothers made three more flights that day the longest flight covered 852 feet, and it lasted 59 seconds. Soon the brothers were building better airplanes they knew flight would change the world.

Proofreading Marks

∧	Add
⊙	Period
ℒ	Take out
≡	Capital letter
/	Small letter

Did you fix the seven run-on sentences?

Write Your Own

WRITE

D *Imagine you are in a hot-air balloon. You look
down and see houses, trees, and other things
and places in your town. Describe how you think some
of these things and places might look from the balloon.*

_____

_____

_____

_____

_____

_____

_____

_____

_____

_____

_____

_____

_____

_____

_____

_____

Proofreading Checklist ☑

❑ *Did you check that each sentence expresses a
complete thought?*

❑ *Did you correct any run-on sentences?*

Sentences (pp. 8–11) *Read each group of words. Write* *sentence* *if it expresses a complete thought. Write* **fragment** *if it does not.*

1. The only animals with feathers. _____

2. All birds have wings. _____

3. Have beautiful colors and sweet songs. _____

Statements and Questions (pp. 12–15) *Add a period (.) or a question mark (?) to end each sentence. Write* **statement** *or* **question** *to tell what kind of sentence it is.*

4. What is a skua _____ _____

5. It lives in the Arctic _____ _____

6. Brown feathers cover its body _____ _____

Commands and Exclamations (pp. 16–19) *Read each sentence. Write* **command** *if it is a command. Write* **exclamation** *if it is an exclamation.*

7. Listen to the bird out on the lake. _____

8. What an amazing sound! _____

9. Watch it dive under the water. _____

Simple Sentences: Subjects (pp. 20–23) *Underline the subject of each sentence.*

10. Many birds move their wings very quickly.

11. The movement produces sound.

12. Hummingbirds beat their wings 60 times a second.

Simple Sentences: Predicates (pp. 24–27) *Underline the predicate of each sentence.*

13. Birds serve many purposes in nature.

14. Hawks eat mice and other pests.

15. Harmful insects are bird food, too.

Compound Sentences (pp. 28–31) *Read each sentence. Write **compound** if it is a compound sentence. Write **not a compound** if it is not a compound sentence.*

16. Penguins are birds, but they cannot fly.   _____

17. They swim fast, and they depend on fish for food.   _____

18. Their wings act as flippers in the chilly water.   _____

Complex Sentences (pp. 32–35) *Read each sentence. Write **complex** if it is a complex sentence. Write **not complex** if it is not a complex sentence.*

19. A pelican's throat is in the shape of a pouch.   _____

20. The bird will make its throat bigger when it is ready to catch fish.   _____

21. Before it can swallow, the pelican must drain the pouch.   _____

Run-on Sentences (pp. 36–39) *Read each group of words. Write **sentence** if it is a correctly written sentence. Write **run-on** if it is a run-on sentence.*

22. The ostrich is the largest bird it can grow to 9 feet tall.   _____

23. Some ostriches can live to be 40 years old.   _____

24. The ostrich cannot fly it is the fastest bird on land.   _____

DIRECTIONS *Fill in the circle next to the sentence that shows the correct use of capital letters and end marks. The first one is done for you.*

1. ○ My aunt trains dogs?
   ○ she is a police officer
   ○ the dogs do many jobs
   ● That is a smart dog!

2. ○ Saul is a search dog
   ○ My aunt trained him.
   ○ are search dogs pets?
   ○ Where do they live

3. ○ Dog trainers work with puppies?
   ○ Puppies must be brave and eager
   ○ Come here.
   ○ What a good little puppy

4. ○ search dogs can be young or old
   ○ what types are best for this work?
   ○ How many lives they must save?
   ○ Dogs work in different ways.

5. ○ search dogs use their noses.
   ○ Follow the trail?
   ○ Do you smell something?
   ○ keep up the good work.

6. ○ a dog has a great sense of smell!
   ○ it's 1000 times stronger than yours?
   ○ I can hardly believe that!
   ○ Do all dogs have such a strong sense of smell.

7. ○ Search dogs can find lost people
   ○ Some people get lost in the woods?
   ○ Can search dogs find them?
   ○ reward dogs for a job well done

8. ○ Each dog has a trainer
   ○ Do they act as partners
   ○ How close they must be?
   ○ Watch them work together.

DIRECTIONS *Read the paragraph, and look carefully at each underlined part. Fill in the circle next to the answer choice that shows the correct use of capital letters and end marks. If the underlined part is already correct, fill in the circle for "Correct as is." The first one is done for you.*

Did you know that many firehouses have <u>Dalmatians? these</u> spotted dogs are
(9)

there to bring good <u>luck this</u> custom began before modern fire engines were
(10)

<u>around. horses</u> pulled fire wagons back <u>then, and</u> Dalmatians acted as watchdogs.
(11)   (12)

They guarded the horses and the wagons from <u>thieves. Firefighters</u> no longer use
(13)

horse-drawn fire <u>wagons but</u> they still think of Dalmatians as firehouse dogs.
(14)

9. ○ Dalmatians. These
  ● Dalmatians? These
  ○ Dalmatians. these
  ○ Correct as is

10. ○ luck This
  ○ luck. This
  ○ luck, this
  ○ Correct as is

11. ○ around Horses
  ○ around, Horses
  ○ around. Horses
  ○ Correct as is

12. ○ then, And
  ○ then? and
  ○ then and
  ○ Correct as is

13. ○ thieves Firefighters
  ○ thieves? Firefighters
  ○ thieves, firefighters
  ○ Correct as is

14. ○ wagons. but
  ○ wagons, but
  ○ wagons, But
  ○ Correct as is

Lesson 9: **Nouns**

LEARN

- A **noun** is a word that names a person, place, or thing.

Person	Place	Thing
teacher	school	folktale
boy	park	cow
sister	forest	seeds

- A sentence can have one or more nouns.

  Our **teacher** read us a **folktale**.
  A poor **boy** lived in a **forest**.
  This **boy** traded a **cow** for some **seeds**.

- Ideas such as **love**, **kindness**, and **courage** are called **abstract nouns**. You cannot see them, but they are still nouns.

  His **courage** and **kindness** were amazing.

PRACTICE

A *Write **person**, **place**, or **thing** to tell what the noun in **dark print** names. The first one is done for you.*

1. A **mother** was angry with her son. _____*person*_____

2. The woman threw the seeds out into the **yard**. _____

3. A huge **beanstalk** began to grow that night. _____

4. This plant soon reached the **sky**. _____

5. The **boy** decided to climb up. _____

6. The boy was above the **clouds** before long. _____

7. A castle filled with **gold** was there. _____

8. The gold once belonged to the boy's **father**. _____

9. A dangerous **giant** was sleeping in the castle. _____

10. How does this **story** end? _____

B *Find the noun or nouns in each sentence. Write the noun or nouns on the line.*

1. A prince is giving a grand ball. _____

2. A poor girl must stay behind. _____

3. Her beauty is enchanting. _____

4. A beautiful dress suddenly appears! _____

5. Slippers made of glass are on her feet! _____

6. A pumpkin turns into a coach! _____

7. The girl arrives at the palace with joy. _____

8. The hours pass quickly at the exciting dance. _____

9. The girl suddenly races from the ballroom. _____

10. A slipper falls off near the door. _____

11. The girl sadly returns to her house. _____

12. How does this famous tale end? _____

C *Write a noun to complete each sentence. Choose a noun from the box, or use a noun of your own.*

Remember 💡
A **noun** names a person, place, thing or idea.

daughter	flowers	food	gold
happiness	hug	king	love
palace	river	statue	stranger

1. A powerful _____ ruled over a rich land.

2. His _____ was full of riches, but this king wanted more.

3. A _____ granted the king an unusual wish one day.

4. Everything the king touched would turn into solid _____.

5. He quickly turned the _____ in his garden into gold.

6. He grew hungry because his _____ turned into gold, too.

7. Then the king's young _____ ran up to him.

8. His _____ for the child was obvious.

9. The father gave the young girl a big _____.

10. The girl became as hard and cold as a _____.

11. The king learned that riches alone did not bring _____.

12. He washed away his golden touch in a _____.

WRITE

D Replace the noun in **dark print** with a more exact noun. Then write the new sentence. The first one is done for you.

1. A **bird** called from a tree.

A robin called from a tree.

2. The **flowers** were blooming.

_____

3. A young girl wanted to visit her sick **relative**.

_____

4. The girl lived in the same **place** as her relative.

_____

5. The girl was wearing a bright red **thing** on her head.

_____

6. The girl carried a straw **box** over her arm.

_____

7. Some delicious **food** was inside.

_____

8. A friendly **worker** in the forest waved to the girl.

_____

9. A hungry **animal** also watched her pass.

_____

Lesson 10: Common and Proper Nouns

LEARN

- A **common noun** names any person, place, or thing.

  The **girl** visited the **building** in the **city**.

- A **proper noun** names a specific person, place, or thing. It may be one or more words.

  Stacey visited the **United States Mint** in **Denver**.

- Proper nouns begin with capital letters. Common nouns do not.

Common	Proper
president	Thomas Jefferson
state	California
building	United States Mint

United States Mint
where coins are made

PRACTICE

A *Match each common noun in Column A with a proper noun in Column B. Write the letter of the proper noun on the line. The first one is done for you.*

A	B
_e_ **1.** country	**a.** Lake Erie
___ **2.** planet	**b.** Thanksgiving
___ **3.** inventor	**c.** Mars
___ **4.** lake	**d.** Thomas Edison
___ **5.** holiday	**e.** Mexico

A	B
____ **6.** city	**f.** Thursday
____ **7.** building	**g.** Spanish
____ **8.** month	**h.** Dallas
____ **9.** language	**i.** Lincoln Memorial
___ **10.** day	**j.** July

B *Read each sentence. Write **common** if the noun in **dark print** is a common noun. Write **proper** if it is a proper noun.*

1. Our money shows famous people and **buildings** from history. _____

2. **Andrew Jackson** appears on our twenty-dollar bill. _____

3. The back of this bill shows the **White House**. _____

4. Other countries show many different **pictures**. _____

5. You can find an **elephant** on some money in India. _____

6. A bill from Norway shows a map of the **North Pole**. _____

7. One country in **Asia** shows schoolchildren on a bill. _____

8. Brazil shows a **sea turtle** in the ocean. _____

9. A leopard is on some bills from **South Africa**. _____

10. Most countries print bills in all the colors of the **rainbow**. _____

C *Max wrote about America's newest quarters. In his report, he wrote five common nouns with capital letters. He also forgot to write five proper nouns with capital letters. Use the proofreading marks in the box to fix the mistakes.*

Remember
Proper nouns begin with capital letters. **Common nouns** do not.

Have you looked carefully at a quarter recently? The front of this coin always shows george Washington, but the back could be a surprise. You might find a Lighthouse, a mountain, or a tree.

Between 1998 and 2008, the United states Mint made fifty new quarters. There is one design for each State. The coins honor the special history and geography of the states.

The rhode Island quarter shows a Sailboat off the coast. The coin for California shows the early explorer John muir. The coin for georgia shows a peach. Minnesota shows people fishing on one of its many Lakes.

These fifty new quarters are fun to collect. They are also a quick way to learn about our Country.

Proofreading Marks

∧	Add
⊙	Period
ℯ	Take out
≡	Capital letter
/	Small letter

Look Back Did you fix five common nouns and five proper nouns?

WRITE

Write Your Own

D Bills and coins often show famous people, places, or things. If you could design a bill or coin for our country, what famous people, places, or things would it show? Sketch your idea in the box below. Then write four or more sentences to describe your bill or coin. Underline the proper nouns in your sentences.

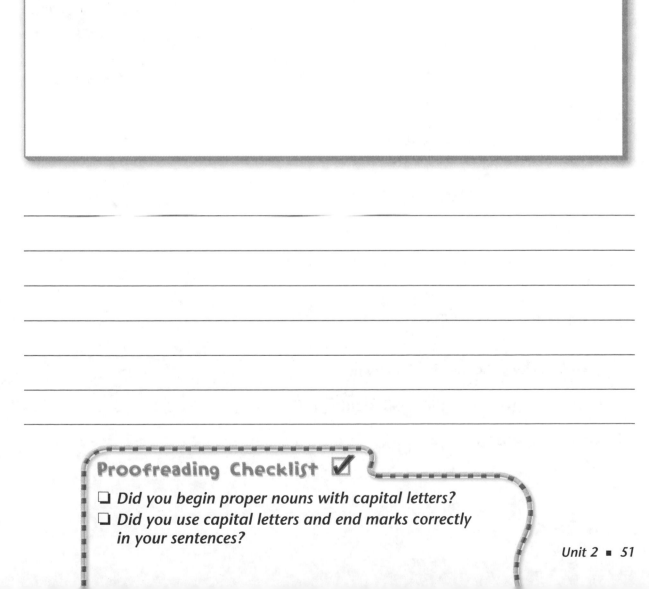

_____

_____

_____

_____

_____

_____

_____

Proofreading Checklist ✓

❏ *Did you begin proper nouns with capital letters?*
❏ *Did you use capital letters and end marks correctly in your sentences?*

Lesson 11: **Nouns in the Subject**

LEARN

■ The **subject** of a sentence tells *whom* or *what* the sentence is about. The main word in the subject is often a **noun**.

In each sentence below, the noun in the subject is in **dark print**.

Subject	Predicate
Many **people**	enjoy basketball.
Jennifer	plays tennis.
My whole **class**	likes baseball.

PRACTICE

A *Read each sentence. Look at the subject in **dark print**. Write the noun in the subject.*

1. **A very popular sport** began in 1891. _____

2. **Its clever inventor** was James Naismith. _____

3. **This coach** needed an indoor ball game for his players. _____

4. **The young man** nailed two baskets to the gym walls. _____

5. **Nine players** were on each team. _____

6. **The new game** had just a few rules at first. _____

7. **Only one person** scored a goal in the first game. _____

8. **Small crowds** gathered to watch the new game. _____

9. Most people loved basketball right away. _____

10. Many athletes play this exciting sport today. _____

B Draw a line between the subject and predicate of each sentence. Then write the noun in the subject. The first one is done for you.

1. Another popular game|started in the 1890s. _____*game*_____

2. Many children enjoyed "indoor tennis" after dinner. _____

3. Their childhoods must be filled with great memories. _____

4. The court was the dining room table. _____

5. Old corks served as balls. _____

6. The paddles were cardboard box lids. _____

7. A company made an indoor tennis kit later. _____

8. Different inventors developed better balls and paddles. _____

9. Many players called the game Ping-Pong. _____

10. The new activity spread around the world. _____

11. Excited fans loved the speed of the game. _____

12. The hobby became a sport. _____

C *Write a noun in the subject to complete each sentence. Choose a noun from the box, or use a noun of your own.*

banners	baseball	bat	batter	crack	crowd
fans	glove	hope	moans	outfielder	pitcher

1. Many happy _____ arrive at the baseball stadium.

2. Colorful _____ wave in the air.

3. A tall _____ throws a fastball over the plate.

4. The skilled _____ swings hard at it.

5. His heavy _____ hits the ball squarely.

6. A loud _____ fills the air.

7. The small _____ flies toward the fence.

8. The cheering _____ thinks it's a home run.

9. Then a speedy _____ jumps high for the ball.

10. His long leather _____ grabs the ball.

11. Loud _____ fill the stadium.

12. Our _____ for a win is still alive.

WRITE

Sometimes two sentences have the same predicate.
Fans cheer loudly. Families cheer loudly.

You can combine the sentences by joining the subjects. The subject of each sentence above is a noun. Use *and* to join the nouns.
<u>Fans</u> **and** <u>families</u> cheer loudly.

D *Each pair of sentences below has the same predicate. Combine the nouns in the subject of each sentence to form one sentence.*

1. Buses arrive in the parking lot. Cars arrive in the parking lot.

_____

2. Friends get out of their cars. Families get out of their cars.

_____

3. Players are ready. Coaches are ready.

_____

4. Cheers shake the gym. Shouts shake the gym.

_____

5. The jumps are amazing! The shots are amazing!

_____

6. Players are excited. Fans are excited.

_____

7. Minutes tick away. Seconds tick away.

_____

 **Go back to the sentences you wrote.
Underline the two nouns in each subject.**

Lesson 12: **Singular and Plural Nouns**

LEARN

A **singular noun** names one person, place, or thing.
A **plural noun** names more than one person, place, or thing.

SINGULAR   I picked an **apple**.
PLURAL   I picked three **apples**.

• Add -*s* to form the plural of most singular nouns.

| SINGULAR | plant | bird | farm |
| PLURAL | plant**s** | bird**s** | farm**s** |

• Add -*es* to form the plural of nouns ending in
s, ch, sh, or *x.*

| SINGULAR | grass | bench | brush | box |
| PLURAL | grass**es** | bench**es** | brush**es** | box**es** |

• Some nouns end in a consonant and *y*. To make
these nouns plural, change the *y* to *i* and add -*es.*

| SINGULAR | baby | butterfly |
| PLURAL | bab**ies** | butterfl**ies** |

PRACTICE

A Write **singular** or **plural** to tell about the noun in **dark print**.
If the noun is singular, also write the plural of the noun.
The first one is done for you.

1. a piece of **fruit**   *singular, fruits*

2. one green **vegetable**   _____

3. a bag of **groceries**   _____

4. a bunch of **grapes**   _____

5. one jar of **jelly**   _____

6. one **business**   _____

7. a picnic **lunch** _____

8. one special **wish** _____

9. a brown **fox** _____

10. a bowl of **pears** _____

B *Write the noun in ( ) that correctly completes each sentence.*

1. Our farm is on a busy _____. (road, roads)

2. People in cars and _____ stop to buy our foods. (bus, buses)

3. One _____ wants fresh corn. (family, families)

4. Green beans grow on those low _____. (bush, bushes)

5. The _____ grow faster than the other vegetables. (radish, radishes)

6. I just dug up a _____ of them. (bunch, bunches)

7. I pick _____ on most June mornings. (strawberry, strawberries)

8. Our _____ get ripe in July. (peach, peaches)

9. The _____ are bigger than ever this year. (cherry, cherries)

10. Many _____ turn orange by September. (pumpkin, pumpkins)

C *Read each clue. Then find the noun in the box that matches it.*
Write the plural of the noun on the line. The first one is done for you.

ax	bee	berry	branch
carrot	daisy	dish	glass
guppy	pony	press	rooster

1. These little juicy fruits can be blue or black.   _____berries_____

2. Apples and pears hang from these things.   _____

3. These orange vegetables grow underground.   _____

4. These birds wake up people on a farm.   _____

5. These farm animals are fun to ride.   _____

6. These tools squeeze apples into cider.   _____

7. You drink fresh cider in these things.   _____

8. These tools chop firewood.   _____

9. These insects make honey.   _____

10. These little fish swim in the pond.   _____

11. You can serve fruits and vegetables on these things.   _____

12. You can pick these to put in a vase.   _____

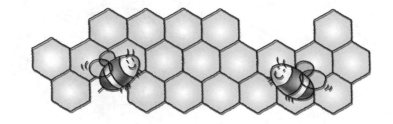

WRITE

D *Imagine you went to a party at a farm. Describe the party. Tell who was there and what foods were served. Tell what games were played and what funny things happened. First write the plural of each noun below. Then use some of them in your description.*

1. batch _____

2. couch _____

3. party _____

4. sandwich _____

5. bunny _____

6. dress _____

7. pie _____

8. wish _____

_____

_____

_____

_____

_____

_____

_____

_____

_____

_____

_____

Proofreading Checklist ✔

❏ *Did you spell each plural noun correctly?*
❏ *Did you use capital letters and end marks correctly in each sentence?*

Lesson 13: **Irregular Plural Nouns**

LEARN

Some nouns have **irregular plurals**. These plurals do not end in -s or -es. In most cases, there is a spelling change in the plural.

Singular	Plural
man	men
woman	women
child	children
goose	geese
mouse	mice
tooth	teeth
foot	feet

In a few cases, the plural noun is the same as the singular noun.

Singular	Plural
deer	deer
sheep	sheep
moose	moose

PRACTICE

A *Write the plural of each noun.*

1. goose _____

2. mouse _____

3. deer _____

4. tooth _____

5. child _____

6. man _____

7. moose _____

9. woman _____

8. foot _____

10. sheep _____

B Complete the rhyming lines. Write the plural of each noun in **dark print**. The first one is done for you.

1. The single noun **man** as a plural is _____*men*_____,

but the plural of **fan** is _____*fans*_____, never *fen*.

2. You may see a small **mouse** or a family of _____,

but the plural of **house** is _____, not *hice*.

3. One bird is a **goose**, and two are called _____,

but the plural of **moose** is _____, never *meese*.

4. I have one left **foot**, and I stand on two _____,

but the plural of **boot** is _____ and not *beet*.

5. The plural of **tooth** is always _____,

but the plural of **booth** is _____, never *beeth*.

6. The single noun **jeep** as a plural is _____,

but the plural of **sheep** is _____, never *sheeps*.

7. The single noun **steer** as a plural is _____,

but the plural of **deer** is _____, never *deers*.

C *This retelling of a fable has eight irregular plural nouns that are spelled incorrectly. Look for the mistakes, and correct them. Use the proofreading marks in the box.*

The Lion and the Mice

An old lion once saw two tiny mouses creeping through his den. Grabbing them, he roared and showed his big tooths.

"Let us go," the mices begged, "and we will pay back your kindness someday."

"How could you ever pay me back?" the lion laughed, but he let them go in the end.

Now this lion sometimes hunted deers in the forest. More often, however, he went after the sheeps near the village. The mans who lived there didn't like that. So they set a trap for the lion.

One day, the two mice heard a loud roaring. The old lion had put his foots in a net and was trapped. Right away, the mice went to work. With their sharp teeths, they chewed through the net. Before long, the lion was free.

Proofreading Marks

∧	Add
⊙	Period
ℓ	Take out
≡	Capital letter
/	Small letter

Did you fix the spelling of eight irregular plural nouns?

WRITE

D Write a story using some of the irregular plural nouns on page 60. You can write about real things that people and animals do. You can also write about silly things that they might do.

 Additional Resources at grammarworkshop.com

_____

_____

_____

_____

_____

_____

_____

_____

Proofreading Checklist ✓

❏ Did you spell each irregular plural noun correctly?
❏ Did you use capital letters and end marks correctly in each sentence?

Lesson 14: **Possessive Nouns**

LEARN

A **possessive noun** shows *who* or *what* owns or has something.

> **The cat that Pam owns is asleep.**
> **Pam's** cat is asleep.

> The den of the lions is crowded.
> The **lions'** den is crowded.

- To make a singular noun possessive, add an apostrophe and an *-s*.

SINGULAR	Pam
SINGULAR POSSESSIVE	Pam**'s**

- To make a plural noun that ends in *-s* possessive, add only an apostrophe.

PLURAL	lions
PLURAL POSSESSIVE	lions**'**

PRACTICE

A *Circle the word that describes the noun in **dark print**. Then write the possessive form of the noun. The first one is done for you.*

1. the pony that **Max** owns   (*singular*)   *plural*   Max's

2. the hamster the **girls** have   *singular*   *plural*   _____

3. the cave of the **bat**   *singular*   *plural*   _____

4. the tunnel of the **badgers**   *singular*   *plural*   _____

5. the hole of the **mouse**   *singular*   *plural*   _____

6. the web of the **spider**   *singular*   *plural*   _____

7. the burrow of the **woodchucks**   *singular*   *plural*   _____

8. the hive of the **bees**   *singular*   *plural*   _____

9. the nest of the **sparrow**   *singular*   *plural*   _____

10. the mound of the **termites**   *singular*   *plural*   _____

B   *Write the possessive form of the noun in ( ) that correctly completes each sentence.*

1. Beavers build their lodges on a _____ quiet water. (lake)

2. The _____ entrances are underwater. (lodges)

3. A _____ stick nest is high in a tree. (squirrel)

4. The _____ height protects the squirrel from many enemies. (nest)

5. _____ underground homes are called warrens. (rabbits)

6. Rabbits dig more tunnels as their ___ _____ numbers grow. (group)

7. Polar bears need shelter from the _____ freezing temperatures. (Arctic)

8. These _____ dens are dug deep into snow banks. (bears)

9. A baby _____ home is unusual. (koala)

10. The baby lives in the _____ pouch. (mother)

Jon wrote about a field trip that his class took. He made eight mistakes when writing possessive nouns. Look for the mistakes, and correct them. Use the proofreading marks in the box.

A possessive noun shows *who* or *what* owns or has something.

∧	Add
⊙	Period
ℰ	Take out
≡	Capital letter
/	Small letter

The field trip our class took to Johnson Park was a success. We found the homes of many animals there.

A robins' grass nest was in an oak tree. The tree's thick branches helped hide the nest. Some wasps nests were hanging in the same tree.

We also saw a woodpeckers' hole in a maple tree. The hole is now a new home for a family of starlings.

We saw a woodchucks burrow near the parks main road. Woodchucks dig down 30 feet or more to make their burrows.

At the stream, we came across some ducklings nest and an otters' den. It was amazing to see how different each animals home is from other homes.

Did you correct eight possessive nouns?

66 ▪ Unit 2

Write Your Own

WRITE

D Rewrite each group of words using a possessive noun. Then write a sentence using the group of words to describe what you might see, hear, feel, or smell in a park or forest. The first one is done for you.

1. the leaves of the trees _____ the trees' leaves _____

The trees' leaves shine in the sunlight. _____

2. the heat of the sun _____

_____

3. the wings of the butterflies _____

_____

4. the chirping of the crickets _____

_____

5. the sound of the wind _____

_____

6. the color of the water _____

_____

7. the smell of the flowers _____

_____

8. the beauty of the sunset _____

_____

Proofreading Checklist ☑

❑ Did you spell the possessive nouns correctly?
❑ Did you use capital letters and end marks correctly in your sentences?

Nouns (pp. 44–47) *Find the noun or nouns in each sentence. Write the noun or nouns on the line.*

1. Most children play tag. _____

2. Many people can join in. _____

3. Hopscotch is popular, too. _____

4. It is an honor to play these games. _____

5. Do your friends jump with ropes? _____

Common and Proper Nouns (pp. 48–51) *Read each sentence. Write **common** if the noun in **dark print** is a common noun. Write **proper** if it is a proper noun.*

6. Soldiers in ancient **Rome** played hopscotch. _____

7. The Romans spread the game throughout **Europe**. _____

8. Children draw hopscotch squares on a **sidewalk**. _____

9. **Players** hop over the squares on one leg. _____

10. People call this game *pico* in **Vietnam**. _____

Nouns in the Subject (pp. 52–55) *Read each sentence. Then look at the subject in **dark print**. Write the noun in the subject.*

11. **Some marbles** are over 5000 years old. _____

12. **These stones** were popular in ancient Egypt. _____

13. **The round balls** are still popular today. _____

14. **Many different games** use marbles. _____

15. **The winning player** keeps the marbles. _____

Singular and Plural Nouns (pp. 56–59) *Read each sentence. Write the plural of each noun in ( ).*

16. Playgrounds in (city) are good places for games. _____

17. Different games of tag have different (rule). _____

18. Draw some (box) to play hopscotch. _____

19. Trees and (bush) come in handy in hide-and-seek. _____

20. Some jump rope (rhyme) are hundreds of years old. _____

Irregular Plural Nouns (pp. 60–63) *Read each sentence. Write the plural of each noun in ( ).*

21. Most (child) enjoy playground games. _____

22. You use one foot in hopscotch but two (foot) in jump rope. _____

23. A fox chases (goose) in a popular game. _____

24. The game of jacks first used small bones of (sheep). _____

25. The game hide-and-seek is like a cat chasing (mouse). _____

Possessive Nouns (pp. 64–67) *Read each sentence. Write the possessive form of the noun in ( ).*

26. My (friends) favorite game is kickball. _____

27. We play in (Jason) backyard. _____

28. I kicked (Toni) ball over the back fence. _____

29. The (players) decision stands. _____

30. Each (neighborhood) rules are different for kickball. _____

DIRECTIONS *Fill in the circle next to the sentence that shows correct spelling and the correct use of capital letters and apostrophes.*

1. ○ My family drove across the united states.

   ○ Our Trip began in Vermont.

   ○ We saw Lake Ontario.

   ○ It is on the Border of New York and Canada.

2. ○ We crossed a Bridge to get to Michigan.

   ○ Detroit is michigan's largest city.

   ○ Lansing is also an important city.

   ○ A Ferry crosses lake Michigan.

3. ○ Minnesota has many beachs.

   ○ We saw deers and moose.

   ○ The skys were deep blue.

   ○ We camped under the branches of a tall pine.

4. ○ Several bridges' cross the Red River.

   ○ That is North Dakota's eastern border.

   ○ Farms and ranchs cover most of North Dakota.

   ○ Farming is this areas' main business.

5. ○ Montana was named for its Mountains.

   ○ Cattle eat the prairie grass's.

   ○ Many towns were miners' camps.

   ○ Rodeos are popular in Montana's citys.

6. ○ Our familys' trip continued through Idaho.

   ○ The mountaines are amazing.

   ○ Ranchers raise sheep in Idaho.

   ○ Potatoes come from Idahos' soil.

7. ○ The Ocean was our journeys' halfway mark.

   ○ The beauty of Washingtons coast cannot be described.

   ○ The worlds' largest ships dock in Washington.

   ○ Ships sailed there from Asia.

8. ○ We headed south for our Trip home.

   ○ We saw amazing butterflys in a desert.

   ○ My parents favorite stop was the Grand Canyon.

   ○ This country's natural treasures are amazing!

Read the paragraph, and look carefully at each underlined part. Fill in the circle next to the answer choice that shows correct spelling and the correct use of capital letters and apostrophes. If the underlined part is already correct, fill in the circle for "Correct as is."

We visited Mount Rushmore in <u>South dakota</u>. It is in the area
(9)
called the Black Hills near Rapid City. Mount Rushmore is one of our

<u>countries' famous monuments</u>. The carving of George <u>Washingtons head</u>
(10)   (11)
is <u>five stories high</u>. The faces of three other great leaders also appear.
(12)
They belong to Thomas Jefferson, Abraham Lincoln, and Theodore

Roosevelt. <u>Workmens with drills</u> and <u>boxs of dynamite</u> spent fourteen
(13)   (14)
years shaping these faces.

9. ○ south dakota
   ○ south Dakota
   ○ South Dakota
   ○ Correct as is

10. ○ countrys famous monuments
   ○ country's famous monuments
   ○ countries famous monuments
   ○ Correct as is

11. ○ Washingtons' head
   ○ Washingtones head
   ○ Washington's head
   ○ Correct as is

12. ○ five story high
   ○ five storys high
   ○ five storyes high
   ○ Correct as is

13. ○ Workmen with drills
   ○ Workmans with drills
   ○ Workmanes with drills
   ○ Correct as is

14. ○ boxes of dynamite
   ○ boxies of dynamite
   ○ box of dynamite
   ○ Correct as is

Lesson 15: **Action Verbs**

LEARN

■ An **action verb** is a word that tells what someone or something does.

A tall tree **sways** in the wind.
Birds **sing** sweetly.
Children **play** under the tree.

■ Every sentence has a verb. The verb is the main word in the predicate. The verb tells what the subject does.

Subject	Predicate
Dad	**builds** a tree house for me.
My friends	**paint** the tree house.
We	**watch** the birds in the tree.

PRACTICE

A Read each sentence. Then look at the predicate in **dark print** Write the action verb.

1. Trees **grow almost everywhere**. _____

2. Many trees **live for hundreds of years**. _____

3. An old tree **shades our house and street**. _____

4. A young tree **adds beauty to our yard**. _____

5. Farmers **pick fruit and nuts from trees**. _____

6. Mills **make lumber and paper from trees**. _____

7. Many people **hike among the trees**. _____

8. My parents **sit under their tree**. _____

9. Birds and animals **build homes in trees**. _____

10. Squirrels **run along tree branches**. _____

B *Draw a line between the subject and predicate of each sentence. Then write the action verb. The first one is done for you.*

1. Sap|flows in a tree's trunk in early spring.   *flows*

2. This sap spreads to all the branches. _____

3. Buds grow on the branches. _____

4. New green leaves burst from the buds. _____

5. The leaves make food for the tree. _____

6. The tree needs water and light, too. _____

7. The leaves give shade on hot summer days. _____

8. Trees lose water through their leaves. _____

9. Cold weather dries the leaves of many trees. _____

10. The green leaves turn yellow, red, and orange. _____

11. All the leaves fall to the ground by winter. _____

12. Snow covers bare branches with soft beauty. _____

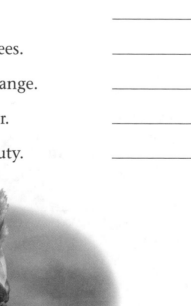

C Write an action verb to complete each sentence. Choose an action verb from the box, or use an action verb of your own.

buys	digs	enjoy	fills	grows	measure
plants	protects	puts	spreads	waters	wraps

1. The Nature Club _____ a tree every spring.

2. Mrs. Lee _____ the little tree at a plant store.

3. James _____ a deep hole with the shovel.

4. Carol _____ the tree in the hole.

5. She _____ the tree's roots in the hole.

6. Then Connie _____ in the hole with soil.

7. Juan _____ heavy paper around the trunk.

8. The paper _____ the tree from insects.

9. One student _____ the tree every day.

10. The tree _____ next to other young trees.

11. We _____ the trees' growth each year.

12. The students _____ this tree project.

WRITE

Additional Resources at
grammarworkshop.com

Sometimes two sentences have the same subject.

Jake draws a tree. Jake colors a tree.

You can combine the sentences by joining the verbs in the predicates.

Use _and_ to join the verbs.

Jake <u>draws</u> **and** <u>colors</u> a tree.

D _Each pair of sentences below has the same subject. Combine the verbs in the predicate of each sentence to form one sentence._

1. Peter sits under a tree. Peter reads under a tree. _____

_____

2. Susan swings under a tree. Susan laughs under a tree. _____

_____

3. Joan builds a birdhouse. Joan hangs a birdhouse. _____

_____

4. Birds find seeds in the house. Birds eat seeds in the house. _____

_____

5. Norm picks peaches from the trees. Norm sells peaches from the trees.

_____

6. Some branches break in the storm. Some branches fall in the storm.

_____

**Go back to each sentence you wrote.
Underline the two verbs in the predicate.**

Lesson 16: Present-Tense Verbs

LEARN

- The **tense** of a verb tells when an action happens. A verb in the **present tense** tells about an action that happens now.

  The girl **reads** a book of proverbs.

- A present-tense verb must match, or agree with, the noun in the subject of the sentence.

  - When the noun in the subject is singular, add -*s* to the verb.

    The proverb **gives** good advice.

  - When the noun in the subject is plural, do not add -*s* to the verb.

    Many proverbs **give** advice.

PRACTICE

A *Write the verb in ( ) that correctly completes each sentence.*

1. Too many cooks _____ the meal. (spoil, spoils)

2. The squeaky wheel _____ the grease. (get, gets)

3. Many hands _____ light work. (make, makes)

4. Tall oaks _____ from tiny acorns. (grow, grows)

5. A rolling stone _____ no moss. (gather, gathers)

6. April showers _____ May flowers. (bring, brings)

7. One good deed _____ another. (deserve, deserves)

8. All roads _____ to Rome. (lead, leads)

9. All good things _____ to an end. (come, comes)

10. Clouds _____ before a storm. (gather, gathers)

B *Write the present tense of the verb in ( ) to correctly complete each sentence.*

1. Good fences _____ good neighbors. (make)

2. Great minds _____ alike. (think)

3. History _____ itself. (repeat)

4. The longest trip _____ with one step. (begin)

5. Two heads _____ better than one. (work)

6. Bad workers _____ their tools. (blame)

7. Every little bit _____ . (help)

8. Every picture _____ a story. (tell)

9. Still waters _____ deep. (run)

10. Actions _____ louder than words. (speak)

C Read this list of proverbs. In five of the proverbs, the verbs do not agree with their subjects. Look for the mistakes, and correct them. Use the proofreading marks in the box.

Room 203's
List of Proverbs

1. The first pizza slice tastes better than the second pizza slice.

2. Great minds agrees with my ideas.

3. April showers delays ball games.

4. Two heads complete homework faster than one.

5. The bell stop a kickball game at the most exciting moment.

6. Small amounts adds up to a lot.

7. Good fences protect us from mean dogs.

8. The noisy child gets the attention.

9. Best friends gets different teachers.

10. Practice makes perfect or close to perfect.

Proofreading Marks

∧	Add
⊙	Period
℮	Take out
≡	Capital letter
/	Small letter

Did you fix five verbs that do not agree with their subjects?

WRITE

D *Replace the verb in **dark print** with a more descriptive verb.
Be sure the verb agrees with the subject. Write the new
sentence. The first one is done for you.*

1. The twins **go** to soccer practice on a bus. _____

The twins ride to soccer practice on a bus.

2. The team members **go** around the field to warm up. _____

_____

3. Terri **moves** for the ball during the practice. _____

_____

4. The ball **moves** toward the goal. _____

_____

5. The goalie **moves** for the ball, but he misses it. _____

_____

6. The coach **says**, "Goal!" _____

_____

7. Terri's friends **say**, "How did you do that?" _____

_____

8. Terri **says**, "Practice makes perfect!" _____

_____

Lesson 17: **More Present-Tense Verbs**

LEARN

A present-tense verb must match, or agree with, the noun in the subject of the sentence.

Follow these rules to make the verb agree.

- **For verbs that end in *ss, ch, sh,* or *x*:**

  - **When the noun in the subject is singular, add *-es*.**
    toss + es = toss**es**
    The family **tosses** away trash.

  - **When the noun in the subject is plural, do not add *-es*.**
    The families **toss** away trash.

- **For verbs that end in a consonant and *y*:**

  - **When the noun in the subject is singular, change *y* to *i* and add *-es*.**
    bury + es = bur**ies**
    The city **buries** the trash.

  - **When the noun in the subject is plural, do not change *y* to *i* or add *-es*.**
    The cities **bury** trash.

PRACTICE

 Write the verb in ( ) that correctly completes each sentence.

1. People _____ all their trash together. (mix, mixes)

2. The mayor _____ about all the trash. (worry, worries)

3. The city _____ on just one landfill. (rely, relies)

4. The trash pile _____ higher and higher. (reach, reaches)

5. Big machines _____ the garbage. (crush, crushes)

6. Workers _____ the landfill carefully. (watch, watches)

7. One expert _____ it will soon be full. (guess, guesses)

8. Our mayor _____ for more landfills. (search, searches)

9. The mayor _____ the problem in her speeches.
(stress, stresses)

10. Every person _____ for an easy solution.
(wish, wishes)

B *Write the present tense of the verb in ( ) to correctly complete each sentence.*

1. The city _____ the recycling problem. (fix)

2. The mayor's office _____ people about recycling. (teach)

3. Her office _____ special garbage cans. (supply)

4. Each family _____ glass, plastic, metal, and paper in separate bins. (toss)

5. A city truck _____ these materials to factories. (rush)

6. One factory _____ plastic into new products. (press)

7. The city's people _____ less now about the trash problem. (worry)

8. The solution _____ the people. (satisfy)

C *This list tells how some students recycle. Read the sentences in the list. Find the six verbs that do not agree with their subjects. Look for the mistakes, and correct them. Use the proofreading marks in the box.*

Ways We Reuse and Recycle

- Dana washes old food containers for leftovers.
- Tyrell carry his own canvas bags to the supermarket.
- Terri pass her old clothes to her younger cousins.
- Juan mixes junk mail with newspapers for recycling.
- Wayne polish the furniture with rags.
- Richard crunch boxes to recycle.
- Lee's dad fix broken toys.
- Maria writes on both sides of a piece of paper.
- Joan patch worn spots in her jeans.

Proofreading Marks

∧	Add
⊙	Period
ℓ	Take out
≡	Capital letter
/	Small letter

Did you fix six verbs that do not agree with their subjects?

WRITE

D Write five sentences that tell some of the ways you
and your family reuse and recycle. Use present-tense
verbs in your sentences. Be sure that the verbs agree with
the subjects. You can use some of the words in the box.

bottles	cans	carry
crunch	crush	fix
newspapers	patch	polish

1. _____

2. _____

3. _____

4. _____

5. _____

Write a brief report to give your opinion about recycling.
Is it a good idea? Why or why not?

_____

_____

_____

_____

_____

Proofreading Checklist ☑

❑ *Did you check if the verbs in your sentences agree*
with the subjects?
❑ *Did you follow the rules for spelling verbs?*

Lesson 18: **Past-Tense Verbs**

LEARN

■ A verb in the **past tense** tells about an action that already happened.

Ellen **visited** the Statue of Liberty last week.
We **waited** a long time for the ferry.

■ Follow these rules to form the past tense.

• **Add -*ed* to most verbs.**
visit + ed = visit**ed**

• **For verbs that end in *e*, drop the *e* and add -*ed*.**
race + ed = rac**ed**

• **For verbs that end in a consonant and *y*, change the *y* to *i* and add -*ed*.**
try + ed = tr**ied**

• **For most verbs that end in one vowel followed by one consonant, double the consonant and add -*ed*.**
step + ed = step**ped**

PRACTICE

A *Write the past tense of each verb.*

1. dry _____

2. vote _____

3. hug _____

4. play _____

5. want _____

6. drop _____

7. hum _____

8. learn _____

9. smile _____

10. worry _____

B *Write the past tense of the verb in ( ) to correctly complete each sentence.*

1. A French man _____ the Statue of Liberty. (plan)

2. A ship _____ the statue to New York Harbor in 1885. (carry)

3. The statue _____ immigrants from faraway lands. (greet)

4. "Lady Liberty" _____ strong feelings. (stir)

5. A bright light _____ from her torch. (glow)

6. Many immigrants _____ in New York in the early 1900s. (arrive)

7. They _____ at the statue from their ships. (stare)

8. More immigrants _____ to the railing to see the statue. (hurry)

9. Some immigrants _____ with happiness. (cry)

10. They _____ for a better future. (hope)

11. Americans _____ a poem at the bottom of the statue in 1903. (place)

12. This poem _____ people to America. (welcome)

C *Ellen wrote this note from the Statue of Liberty. She spelled six past-tense verbs incorrectly. Find the mistakes, and fix them. Use the proofreading marks in the box*

Dear Mom,

The ferry stoped at Liberty Island, and we hurryed into the Statue of Liberty. I climbed the stairs to a lookout point. Dad tried the elevator. We looked at the ships out in the harbor.

We scrambleed up the stairs to the crown. I counted 154 steps on the way up. I studied the wall of the statue, too. I spoted the iron frame and the thin copper skin in a few places. The view from the crown really moveed me. I enjoyed this trip so much!

Love,

Ellen

Proofreading Marks	
∧	Add
⊙	Period
ℯ	Take out
≡	Capital letter
/	Small letter

Did you spell six past-tense verbs correctly?

LOOK Back

WRITE

D Write a postcard to a friend or relative. Tell about a place you visited. Describe what you saw. Give some facts about the place, too. Be sure to use past-tense verbs in your sentences.

Dear _____ ,

_____

_____

_____

_____

_____

_____

Love,

_____

Proofreading Checklist ☑

❏ Did you use past-tense verbs in your sentences?
❏ Did you follow the rules for spelling past-tense verbs?

Lesson 19: Future-Tense Verbs

LEARN

- A verb in the **future tense** tells about an action that is going to happen. Use the word *will* to form the future tense.

  Tomorrow, **I will look** at the moon.

- The present, past, and future tenses are **simple tenses**. They tell about action that happens now (in the present), in the past, and in the future.

  PRESENT   Tonight, I **look** at the moon.
  PAST   Last night, I **looked** at the moon.
  FUTURE   Tomorrow night, I **will look** at the moon.

PRACTICE

A *Read each sentence. Write **present, past,** or **future** to tell the tense of the verb in **dark print**. The first one is done for you.*

1. I **borrowed** a book about planets from the library yesterday.   *past*

2. I **started** the first chapter early this morning.   _____

3. I **will learn** many interesting facts from this book.   _____

4. A spacecraft from our country **visited** another planet.   _____

5. Ice chunks and rocks **form** the beautiful rings around Saturn.   _____

6. Sixty-three moons **circle** Jupiter.   _____

7. I **will read** until lunchtime.   _____

8. My dad **calls** me for lunch now.   _____

9. I **will tell** him some facts about the planets.   _____

10. I **will read** more of my book this afternoon.   _____

B *Rewrite each sentence about the future. Use the future tense of the verb in ( ). The first one is done for you.*

1. Everyday life (seem) very different in 2150. _____

   Everyday life will seem very different in 2150.

2. People (fly) through the air on flying boards. _____

   _____

3. Air travel tunnels (stretch) from city to city. _____

   _____

4. Our cars (run) on energy from the stars. _____

   _____

5. Libraries (look) like giant computers. _____

   _____

6. Our pens (use) beams of light instead of ink. _____

   _____

7. Our teachers (appear) on large computers. _____

   _____

8. Many children (attend) space camp in summer. _____

   _____

9. Young people (move) to other planets at age 21. _____

   _____

10. Countries (solve) their problems in peaceful ways. _____

    _____

C *Read this list of ideas from 1900 about the future. The writer did not put six verbs in the future tense. Look for the mistakes, and correct them. Use the proofreading marks in the box.*

Remember
Use the word *will* to form the future tense.

- Automobiles will cost less than horses.

- Refrigerators keep food fresh with liquid air.

- Someone will build a building 100 stories high.

- People cooled their homes with machines.

- All city traffic travels below or high above the ground.

- Loud noise will disappear from large cities.

- Doctors looked deep inside the human body.

- Invisible light allowed the doctors to do this.

- People listened to concerts over their telephones.

- Air tubes will deliver mail to people's houses.

Proofreading Marks

∧	Add
⊙	Period
ℰ	Take out
≡	Capital letter
/	Small letter

Did you put six verbs in the future tense?

Write Your Own

WRITE

D *What do you think life will be like in 150 years? Write one idea about each topic. Be sure to use a verb in the future tense in each sentence. Check a dictionary if you need help spelling a word.*

School

_____

_____

People's Houses

_____

_____

Neighborhoods

_____

_____

Sports

_____

_____

Jobs

_____

_____

Trees

_____

_____

Proofreading Checklist ☑

❏ *Did you use a future-tense verb in each sentence?*
❏ *Did you use **will** to form each future-tense verb?*

Lesson 20: Linking Verbs

LEARN

■ A linking verb does not show action. A **linking verb** tells what someone or something is.

Dani **is** my best friend.
Costume parties **are** fun.

■ The verb *be* is a common linking verb. It has different forms. Use the form that agrees with the subject of the sentence.

Subject	Present Tense	Past Tense
singular noun	is	was
plural noun	are	were
I	am	was
you	are	were
he, she, it	is	was
we, they	are	were

PRESENT   My costume **is** ready now.

PAST   My costume **was** not ready yesterday.

PRACTICE

A *Underline the linking verb in each sentence. Write **present** or **past** to tell the tense of the verb.*

1. Each guest at the party is a mystery at first. _____

2. I am the big T. rex. _____

3. I was a pirate last year. _____

4. Sara is a knight in armor this year. _____

5. You were a purple frog last year. _____

6. Two people are in an elephant costume.　＿＿＿＿＿＿＿＿

7. Jodi is probably the elephant's head.　＿＿＿＿＿＿＿＿

8. They were in a robot costume last year.　＿＿＿＿＿＿＿＿

9. Part of the robot costume was a garbage can.　＿＿＿＿＿＿＿＿

10. We are such clever costume makers!　＿＿＿＿＿＿＿＿

B *Underline the linking verb in ( ) that correctly completes each sentence.
Write **present** or **past** to tell the tense of the verb.*

1. Dani (is, are) the host of the party.　＿＿＿＿＿＿＿＿

2. Dani (is, are) a clown.　＿＿＿＿＿＿＿＿

3. The clown costume (is, are) very colorful.　＿＿＿＿＿＿＿＿

4. My T. rex tail (was, were) too long!　＿＿＿＿＿＿＿＿

5. I (was, were) in everyone's way.　＿＿＿＿＿＿＿＿

6. The guests (is, are) hungry and thirsty.　＿＿＿＿＿＿＿＿

7. Their masks (is, are) off now.　＿＿＿＿＿＿＿＿

8. The twins (was, were) in the elephant costume.　＿＿＿＿＿＿＿＿

9. Jodi (was, were) the back of the elephant.　＿＿＿＿＿＿＿＿

10. The party food (is, are) tasty.　＿＿＿＿＿＿＿＿

11. Our costumes (was, were) funny.　＿＿＿＿＿＿＿＿

12. The party (was, were) a big success.　＿＿＿＿＿＿＿＿

C *Here is a letter Alan wrote. He made seven mistakes using linking verbs. Use the proofreading marks to correct the mistakes.*

Remember
Use the form of the verb *be* that agrees with the subject of the sentence.

Dear Grandma and Grandpa,

This picture is of me in my dinosaur costume. I love dinosaurs, and I were a T. rex for a costume party. Mom was happy to make the costume for me. Well, at least she was willing to help me with it.

The costume are mainly cardboard. The tail alone are six feet long. I covered the cardboard with spray foam. It is all bumpy. Dinosaurs was lizards after all.

Finally, I painted the costume green and red. The dinosaurs in books is always gray and brown, but I bet dinosaurs was more colorful than that. Anyway, it were for a party.

I had a lot of fun as a dinosaur!

Love,

Alan

Proofreading Marks

∧	Add
⊙	Period
℘	Take out
=	Capital letter
/	Small letter

 Did you fix seven linking verbs?

WRITE

D *Draw a picture of yourself in a costume. It can be a costume that you once wore. It can be one that you would like to make someday.*

Write about your costume. Tell what it is and what it is made from. Tell why you like it, too. Use linking verbs in some of your sentences.

_____

_____

_____

_____

_____

_____

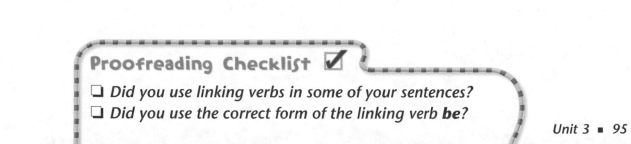

Proofreading Checklist ☑

❏ *Did you use linking verbs in some of your sentences?*
❏ *Did you use the correct form of the linking verb* **be***?*

Lesson 21: **Main Verbs and Helping Verbs**

LEARN

- Sometimes a verb is more than one word.

  main verb
  ↓
  James **is visiting** an arts festival.
  ↑
  helping verb

The most important word is the **main verb**. In the sentence above, *visiting* is the main verb.

The **helping verb** helps the main verb tell about the action. It comes before the main verb. In the sentence above, *is* is the helping verb.

- The verbs *am, is, are, was, were, has, have, had,* and *will* are common helping verbs.

  A large crowd **has gathered** at the festival.
  Many artists **are showing** their paintings.
  Musicians **have played** music, too.
  James **will enjoy** the arts festival.

PRACTICE

A *Draw one line under the helping verb. Draw two lines under the main verb.*

1. are working

2. has finished

3. will return

4. am hurrying

5. was eating

6. had answered

7. have laughed

8. is coming

9. were singing

10. has followed

B *Read each sentence. Write the helping verb and main verb on the line.*

1. I am enjoying the arts festival. _____

2. An artist is painting a beautiful landscape. _____

3. She had sketched the scene yesterday. _____

4. I had watched her for a long time. _____

5. She is adding clouds to the sky now. _____

6. I will paint like her some day. _____

7. Some actors have presented a play. _____

8. The stage curtain has closed now. _____

9. The audience was cheering loudly. _____

10. Some people are clapping still. _____

11. Those dancers were practicing earlier. _____

12. They will perform next. _____

C Write a helping verb and a main verb to complete each sentence. Choose verbs from the box, or use verbs of your own.

am going	are moving	is ending	is enjoying
is wearing	has started	have gathered	was playing
were practicing	will attend	will begin	will read

1. The dance _____ at last.

2. Two dancers _____ like butterflies.

3. The audience _____ their graceful movements.

4. Now some people _____ by the pond.

5. Soon a well-known poet _____ aloud there.

6. I _____ to listen to her poetry.

7. A musician _____ a trumpet a few minutes ago.

8. Some other musicians _____, too.

9. The lead singer _____ a beautiful gown.

10. The concert _____ soon.

11. This arts festival _____ as a great success!

12. I _____ the festival again next year.

WRITE

Write Your Own

D Make up a sentence to answer each question. Include both a helping verb and a main verb in each sentence you write. Then underline the helping verb and the main verb. The first one is done for you.

1. What picture have you painted lately? _____

I <u>have painted</u> a picture of Lake Cedar in winter. _____

2. What colors have you used? _____

_____

3. What sport has your class learned? _____

_____

4. How many weeks have the students practiced soccer? _____

_____

5. What kinds of books are you reading these days? _____

_____

6. Who is reading the longest book? _____

_____

7. What have you borrowed from the library? _____

_____

8. Who is planning a school concert? _____

_____

Proofreading Checklist ✓

❏ *Did you answer each question with a complete sentence?*
❏ *Did you use a helping verb and a main verb in wweach sentence?*

Lesson 22: **Using *Has, Have, Had***

LEARN

The verbs *has, have,* and *had* are helping verbs. They help the main verb tell about an action in the past. Be sure to use a helping verb that agrees with the subject of the sentence.

- Use *has* with a singular noun in the subject and with *he, she,* or *it.*

   The rain **has started**.
   It **has rained** for hours.

- Use *have* with a plural noun in the subject and with *I, you, we,* or *they.*

   My parents **have prepared** for storms.
   I **have placed** a flashlight in my room.

- Use *had* with a singular or plural noun in the subject.

   A neighbor **had called** my family.
   Our neighbors **had listened** to a weather report.

PRACTICE

A Circle *yes* or *no* to tell if the helping verb agrees with the subject of the sentence.

1. We have closed all the windows.   *yes*   *no*

2. Our roof have leaked during a storm last month.   *yes*   *no*

3. My mom has placed a bucket under the leaky spot.   *yes*   *no*

4. My parents has packed a storm kit.   *yes*   *no*

5. My dad has included a pet kit with food and treats. *yes*   *no*

6. We have settled in a room with no windows.   *yes*   *no*

7. My sister has played a game for hours by flashlight.   *yes*   *no*

8. I has completed a puzzle with 500 pieces.   *yes*   *no*

9. The lights has turned on again.   *yes*   *no*

10. The storm have ended.   *yes*   *no*

B *Draw a line under the helping verb in ( ) that correctly completes each sentence.*

1. The city (have, had) learned about the dry forests.

2. Forest workers (has, had) worried about fires.

3. The lightning (have, had) sparked a fire.

4. Strong winds (has, had) started to blow.

5. The blaze (have, had) spread over many miles.

6. Many firefighters (has, have) reached the forest.

7. A helicopter (has, have) dumped water on the fire.

8. All these efforts (has, have) stopped the fires.

9. I (has, have) watched all this on television.

10. My brother (has, have) admired the brave firefighters.

C *Here is part of a make-believe story about a girl in a storm. In seven of the sentences, the helping verbs **has** and **have** do not agree with their subjects. Find the mistakes, and use the proofreading marks to correct them.*

Proofreading Marks

∧	Add
⊙	Period
ℒ	Take out
≡	Capital letter
/	Small letter

A girl named Dorothy lives on a farm in Kansas. The wind from a terrible storm have picked up Dorothy and her dog Toto. The storm have dropped them in the land of Oz.

Dorothy wants to return home. She have traveled on a yellow brick road to Emerald City. Scarecrow, Tin Man, and Lion has walked with Dorothy. Scarecrow has wished for a brain. Tin Man have wanted a heart. Lion has needed courage. They has looked for help in Emerald City.

Dorothy clicks together the heels of her red slippers. She have returned safely to Kansas!

Did you make seven helping verbs agree with their subjects?

Scene from *The Wizard of Oz*

WRITE

D *Have you ever experienced a powerful storm? Was there snow, thunder, or very heavy rain? Write a story telling about the storm. Use the helping verbs **has, have,** and **had** with main verbs to tell what you saw, heard, and did. You can also write a make-believe story about a storm.*

_____

_____

_____

_____

_____

_____

_____

_____

_____

_____

_____

_____

_____

Proofreading Checklist ☑

❑ *Did you use **has, have,** or **had** with main verbs in some of your sentences?*

❑ *Did you check if the helping verbs agree with the subjects of the sentences?*

Lesson 23: Irregular Verbs

LEARN

Irregular verbs do not add *-ed* to form the past tense.
Instead they have special spellings for the past tense.
Their spellings may also change when they are used
with *has, have,* or *had.*

PRESENT	I **run** in the race.
PAST	I **ran** in the race.
WITH *HAVE*	I **have run** in races.

There are many irregular verbs. Here are six of them.

Present	Past	With *has, have,* or *had*
run	ran	has, have, or had run
come	came	has, have, or had come
go	went	has, have, or had gone
bring	brought	has, have, or had brought
take	took	has, have, or had taken
eat	ate	has, have, or had eaten

PRACTICE

A *Underline the verb in ( ) that correctly completes each sentence.*

1. We have (went, gone) to an amazing race in Boston.

2. Runners had (come, came) from all over the world.

3. Some people have (run, ran) the 26-mile race many times.

4. Others (run, ran) it for the first time yesterday.

5. Most runners had (ate, eaten) nothing before the race.

6. A group (bring, brought) water for the runners.

7. Wheelchair racers (took, taken) part in the race, too.

8. The race has (took, taken) this route for over 100 years.

9. The excitement has (bring, brought) out large crowds.

10. Yesterday's winner (run, ran) the race in 2 hours and 20 minutes.

B *Write the correct past form of the verb in ( ) to complete each sentence.*

1. In 1925, sled dogs _____ a different kind of race in Alaska. (run)

2. The dogs _____ all the way from Anchorage to Nome. (go)

3. They ___ _____ medicine to stop a serious illness. (bring)

4. The 500-mile trip _____ many days to complete. (take)

5. Along the way, the dogs _____ fish and meat. (eat)

6. The lead dog _____ down in history. (go)

7. Since 1973, people have _____ to Alaska to race dogsleds. (come)

8. These dog teams have _____ the same route as the famous 1925 team. (take)

9. They have _____ through blizzards and very cold temperatures. (run)

10. Dogsled racing has _____ much excitement to Alaska. (bring)

Balto, the lead dog

Remember 💡
The spelling of an irregular verb changes in the past tense and may change when used with *has, have,* or *had.*

Funny Races Are a Big Hit at Fieldcrest School

More than 100 students came to Liberty Park yesterday for the field day races. Most bringed their families along. Students ran in the races and then eat picnic lunches.

The sack race was the first event. Students climbed into sacks and hopped down the field. Terri Choi taked first place. She gone down the field in 14 seconds flat.

The three-legged race come next. Pairs of students raced with their legs tied together. Eric Diaz and Ray Biggs came in first. They had ran this race before, and they knew how to do it.

The egg race was popular, too. The runners had took hard-boiled eggs and put them on spoons. Then they raced around the track holding them. You were out if you dropped your egg. Al Moody finally won the egg race. All the remaining racers had dropped their eggs by that time, and some had ate them, too!

Proofreading Marks	
∧	Add
⊙	Period
ℰ	Take out
≡	Capital letter
/	Small letter

Look Back **Did you fix eight mistakes with irregular verbs?**

Write Your Own

WRITE

D Write some sentences about a funny race that you made up for your friends. Use the sentence starters below. Use the correct past form of the verb in ( ). The first one is done for you.

1. The race I invented (take) _____

The race I invented took an hour. _____

2. We (run) _____

_____

3. We stopped every ten minutes and (eat) _____

_____

4. Many neighbors (come) _____

_____

5. The neighbors (bring) _____

_____

6. The local newspaper (take) _____

_____

7. We (go) _____

_____

8. We also had (eat) _____

_____

Proofreading Checklist ✓

❏ *Did you use the correct past forms of irregular verbs?*
❏ *Did you use the correct from of the verb with **has**, **have**, and **had**?*

Lesson 24: **More Irregular Verbs**

LEARN

The verbs *say, see, give, write, begin,* and *know* are also irregular. They do not add *-ed* to form the past tense. They have special spellings for the past tense and when used with *has, have,* or *had*.

PRESENT   I **begin** a good story.

PAST   I **began** a good story.

WITH *HAVE*   I **have begun** a good story.

Present	Past	With *has, have,* or *had*
say	said	has, have, or had said
see	saw	has, have, or had seen
give	gave	has, have, or had given
write	wrote	has, have, or had written
begin	began	has, have, or had begun
know	knew	has, have, or had known

PRACTICE

A *Underline the verb in ( ) that correctly completes each sentence.*

1. People have always (knew, known) that records are important.

2. People (began, begun) to write things down over 5000 years ago.

3. People had (wrote, written) on clay.

4. Perhaps you have (saw, seen) clay books in museums.

5. People also (wrote, written) on animal skins long ago.

6. Egypt (gave, given) us the first paper.

7. Not many people (knew, known) how to write long ago.

8. Few people had (saw, seen) a book back then.

9. Writing has (gave, given) people many ideas.

10. Many people have (say, said) writing was a very important invention.

B *Write the correct past form of the verb in ( ) to complete each sentence.*

1. People _____ using printing presses during the 1400s. (begin)

2. This new invention _____ people many more books. (give)

3. Suddenly, the world _____ a big change. (see)

4. By reading, people _____ much more than before. (know)

5. People _____ more and more books. (write)

6. Businesses have _____ a change in writing. (see)

7. Office workers have _____ on typewriters since the 1870s. (write)

8. Workers _____ using copy machines in the 1930s. (begin)

9. Computers have _____ people another way to write. (give)

10. Some people have _____ our handwriting may get worse. (say)

C Emily wrote this book report. She made seven mistakes with the past forms of irregular verbs. Find the mistakes, and use the proofreading marks to correct them.

Ramona Quimby Stories

Beverly Cleary's Ramona Quimby stories always make me laugh. In one story, Ramona had began going to a new school. She was not happy. She had knew everyone in her old school. Now, she seen only strangers.

The year begun badly. First, Ramona broke a raw egg on her head by mistake. Her teacher seen it, and she said Ramona was a show-off. Then Ramona threw up in class. Ramona known her teacher thought she was a pest.

One day, Ramona was home because she was sick. She didn't want to go back to school. Then her classmates write her Get Well cards. That made her feel better, and her school year got better, too.

I enjoyed this story because I'm a lot like Ramona. I started a new school recently, too. I also know what it's like to make silly mistakes in school.

Proofreading Marks	
∧	Add
⊙	Period
ℓ	Take out
≡	Capital letter
/	Small letter

LOOK Back **Did you fix seven mistakes with irregular verbs?**

WRITE

D *Complete the book report below with the past forms of the irregular verbs on page 108. Then write your opinion about the book. Try to use past forms of irregular verbs in your sentences.*

Beverly Cleary has _____ many books about a girl named Ramona Quimby. In <u>Ramona's World</u>, Ramona had _____ the school year. She _____ she wanted to find a new best friend. She found Daisy!

Ramona also liked a classmate named Danny. She had _____ him in the playground. Sometimes she fought with him, but sometimes they were friends.

At home, Ramona had to put up with a new baby. She had to put up with her older sister Beezus, too. Ramona rolled her eyes every time Beezus _____ something in French.

_____

_____

_____

_____

Proofreading Checklist ✔

❑ *Did you use the correct past forms of irregular verbs?*
❑ *Did you use the correct form of the verb with **has**, **have**, and **had**?*

Lesson 25: **Contractions with *Not***

LEARN

A **contraction** is two words written as one. An apostrophe (') takes the place of one or more letters that are left out. Some contractions are formed by joining a verb and the word *not*.

> does + **not** = **doesn't**
> A wet sleeping bag **doesn't** make a good bed!

Contractions with *not*			
is not	**isn't**	do not	**don't**
are not	**aren't**	does not	**doesn't**
was not	**wasn't**	did not	**didn't**
were not	**weren't**	cannot	**can't**
has not	**hasn't**	could not	**couldn't**
have not	**haven't**	should not	**shouldn't**
had not	**hadn't**	would not	**wouldn't**
will not	**won't**		

Notice that the spelling of *will* changes when it is combined with *not* to form the contraction *won't*.

PRACTICE

A *Write the contraction for each pair of words.*

1. has not _____

2. does not _____

3. would not _____

4. had not _____

5. are not _____

6. will not _____

7. were not _____

8. is not _____

9. could not _____

10. cannot _____

B *Write a contraction for the pair of words in ( ) to complete each sentence.*

1. Our first camping trip _____ a success. (was not)

2. We _____ find the camping area until dark. (did not)

3. Then we _____ put up our tent. (could not)

4. Dad _____ packed the tent poles. (had not)

5. "The ground _____ dry," I said. (is not)

6. "We _____ sleep on the ground," Mom said. (cannot)

7. "A little water _____ hurt us," Dad said. (will not)

8. "Besides, we _____ have any other choice," Dad added. (do not)

9. We _____ able to sleep at all that night. (were not)

10. We _____ gone camping since. (have not)

11. We _____ plan another camping trip. (should not)

12. I _____ want another night like that! (would not)

C *This list of rules was posted at a camp. Eight contractions in the rules are written incorrectly. Find the mistakes, and use the proofreading marks to correct them.*

ATTENTION CAMPERS!

🐟 Wild animals arent' pets. Don't feed them!

🐟 Rowboats and canoes wont be allowed on the lake after dark.

🐟 Lake water is'nt safe to drink. Don't drink water you havent boiled.

🐟 Lifeguards willn't be on duty after 6:00 P.M.

🐟 Campers should't take shelter under trees during storms.

🐟 Do'nt hike on private land.

🐟 Camp managers can'ot be responsible for any items left in tents.

Proofreading Marks

∧	Add
⊙	Period
ℒ	Take out
≡	Capital letter
/	Small letter

Off Duty at 6:00 P.M.

LOOK Back

Did you correct eight contractions that were written incorrectly?

Write Your Own

WRITE

D Imagine that you were on a camping trip that did not go well. Use the sentence starters below to write to a friend about the trip. Write a contraction for the words in **dark print**. The first one is done for you.

1. The story of our camping trip **is not** _____

_____

2. The camp **was not** _____

_____

3. My family **had not** _____

_____

4. Our food **did not** _____

_____

5. Our sleeping bags **were not** _____

_____

6. We **could not** _____

_____

7. We **should not** _____

_____

8. We **would not** _____

_____

Proofreading Checklist ☑

❏ *Did you use a contraction in each sentence?*
❏ *Did you use an apostrophe in each contraction to show where a letter or letters were left out?*

Action Verbs (pp. 72–75) *Write the action verb in each sentence.*

1. People celebrate many holidays.

    _____

2. Sometimes people march in parades.

    _____

3. People fly flags for some holidays.

    _____

Present-Tense Verbs (pp. 76–83) *Write the present tense of each verb in ( ) to correctly complete each sentence.*

4. Earth Day (come) on April 22.

    _____

5. People (remember) the environment on this day.

    _____

6. My uncle (teach) me about trees.

    _____

Past-Tense Verbs (pp. 84–87) *Write the past tense of each verb in ( ) to correctly complete each sentence.*

7. One holiday (start) as an honor for only George Washington.

    _____

8. People (decide) to include Abraham Lincoln on Presidents' Day, too.

    _____

9. Our class (study) the lives of both Washington and Lincoln.

    _____

Future-Tense Verbs (pp. 88–91) *Write the future tense of the verb in ( ) to correctly complete each sentence.*

10. Valentine's Day (come) next Wednesday.

    _____

11. My friends (make) colorful cards.

    _____

12. Margaret (send) 12 Valentine cards.

    _____

Linking Verbs (pp. 92–95) *Underline the linking verb in ( ) to correctly complete each sentence. Write **present** or **past** to tell the tense of the verb.*

13. The first Independence Day (was, were) in 1776.   _____

14. Fireworks (was, were) part of the Fourth of July holiday by 1800.   _____

15. This holiday (is, are) still a happy and noisy event today.   _____

Main Verbs and Helping Verbs (pp. 96–103) *In each sentence, draw one line under the helping verb. Draw two lines under the main verb.*

16. Few people have celebrated Left-handers Day.

17. This unusual August 13 event has honored left-handers.

18. Lefties were enjoying the games and events last year.

Irregular Verbs (pp. 104–111) *Write the verb in ( ) that correctly completes each sentence*

19. Peter McGuire (bring, brought) us Labor Day.   _____

20. He had (wrote, written) about the needs of workers for years.   _____

21. The September holiday (began, begun) in 1882.   _____

Contractions with *Not* (pp. 112–115) *Read each sentence. Write the words in **dark print** as a contraction.*

22. Early colonists **could not** be sure of a good harvest.   _____

23. It **is not** hard to see why they celebrated a good harvest in the fall.   _____

24. Thanksgiving **was not** a national holiday until 1863.   _____

DIRECTIONS *Fill in the circle next to the sentence that shows the correct spelling and use of verbs or contractions.*

1. ○ My classmates wants to bake bread.

○ Ms. Clark has wrote a recipe on the board.

○ Our teacher explains the recipe, too.

○ The class need three cups of flour.

2. ○ Ms. Clark washs her hands.

○ All the students wash, too.

○ Rita measure the flour.

○ The cooking class has began.

3. ○ Dan reachs for the warm water.

○ Karen cant open the baking powder.

○ Jed open it.

○ Some powder spills on the floor.

4. ○ I am helping, too.

○ I adds some salt.

○ Ms. Clark has gave a spoon to Mei.

○ Mei stired oil slowly into the dough.

5. ○ Ms. Clark rubed flour on her hands.

○ Then she placed the dough on a board.

○ Now Ms. Clark punchs the dough in the center.

○ The students has watched closely.

6. ○ The warm dough rise slowly.

○ I didnt' know it took so long.

○ Ms. Clark kneads the dough again.

○ The air rushs out all at once.

7. ○ The time had came to bake the bread.

○ Max press the dough into a pan.

○ Ms. Clark gone over to the oven.

○ We won't have to wait long.

8. ○ A delicious smell fill the room.

○ The bread is ready at last.

○ Every student has ate a piece.

○ The students wishes that all bread was homemade.

DIRECTIONS *Read the paragraphs, and look carefully at each underlined part. Fill in the circle next to the answer choice that shows the correct spelling and use of verbs or contractions. If the underlined part is already correct, fill in the circle for "Correct as is."*

Some people <u>dont like baking bread</u>, but millions of people love it.
  (9)

All you have to do is find the right recipe. Some recipes <u>is hard to</u>

<u>follow</u>, but most aren't. The results <u>was usually good</u> if you follow the
 (10)   (11)
recipe carefully.

You <u>willn't buy bread</u> at a store again once you are successful with
    (12)

baking bread. Homemade bread <u>tastes better</u> than bread from the store.
                                      (13)

I <u>known</u> that from experience.
   (14)

9. ○ do'nt like baking bread
  ○ dont' like baking bread
  ○ don't like baking bread
  ○ Correct as is

10. ○ are hard to follow
  ○ was hard to follow
  ○ were hard to follow
  ○ Correct as is

11. ○ is usually good
  ○ are usually good
  ○ were usually good
  ○ Correct as is

12. ○ will 'nt buy bread
  ○ wont' buy bread
  ○ won't buy bread
  ○ Correct as is

13. ○ taste better
  ○ tastees better
  ○ tasted better
  ○ Correct as is

14. ○ I know
  ○ I have knew
  ○ I has known
  ○ Correct as is

Lesson 26: Adjectives

LEARN

Adjectives describe, or tell about, nouns. Adjectives add details to your writing.

- Some adjectives tell *what kind*.

  Philadelphia is an **old** city.
  Philadelphia has an **interesting** history.

- Some adjectives tell *how many*.

  Philadelphia has **many** museums.
  One museum is named after Ben Franklin.

An adjective usually comes before the noun it describes.

PRACTICE

A *Underline the adjective that describes the noun in **dark print**. Then circle the words that tell about the adjective.*

1. Ben Franklin is a famous **man**.   *what kind*   *how many*

2. He was born in 1706 in colonial **Boston**.   *what kind*   *how many*

3. Ben was the fifteenth of seventeen **children**.   *what kind*   *how many*

4. He became a printer's assistant at a young **age**. *what kind*   *how many*

5. Ben ran away with just three **cents** in his pocket. *what kind*   *how many*

6. He made Philadelphia his new **home**.   *what kind*   *how many*

7. He worked hard and became a successful **printer**. *what kind*   *how many*

8. He printed an almanac for twenty-five **years**.   *what kind*   *how many*

9. An almanac is a book of different **facts**.   *what kind*   *how many*

10. Ben's fame spread throughout the thirteen **colonies**.   *what kind*   *how many*

B *Find and underline the adjective in each sentence. Then write the adjective and the noun it describes on the lines. The first one is done for you.*

	Adjective	**Noun**
1. Ben Franklin's almanac reached <u>many</u> readers.	many	readers
2. An almanac includes important dates.		
3. Some almanacs tell about the weather.		
4. Ben's almanac gave helpful advice.		
5. People eagerly read every issue.		
6. They looked for Ben's wise sayings.		
7. Here are several examples.		
8. Two wrongs don't make a right.		
9. Lost time is never found again.		
10. Ben was a curious man.		
11. He created useful inventions.		
12. People loved his clever ideas.		

Ben Franklin invented the lightning rod.

C *Here are some famous old sayings. Write an adjective to complete each one. Choose an adjective from the box, or use an adjective of your own. The clue in ( ) will help you. The first one is done for you.*

Remember 💡
An **adjective** can describe a noun by telling *how many* or *what kind.*

early	few	glass	good	old
one	silver	small	some	two

1. Don't put all your eggs in _____ *one* _____ basket. (*how many*)

2. You have to break a _____ eggs to make an omelet. (*how many*)

3. People in _____ houses should not throw stones. (*what kind*)

4. Every cloud has a _____ lining. (*what kind*)

5. Every garden has _____ weeds. (*how many*)

6. Good things come in _____ packages. (*what kind*)

7. You can't teach an _____ dog new tricks. (*what kind*)

8. No news is _____ news. (*what kind*)

9. _____ heads are better than one. (*how many*)

10. The _____ bird gets the worm. (*what kind*)

WRITE

Sometimes you can combine a pair of related sentences to make your writing smoother. To make the two sentences below less choppy, move the adjective in the second sentence to the first sentence.

It was a day in July in 1776. It was **hot**.
It was a **hot** day in July in 1776.

The sentences in each pair below can be combined. Find the adjective in the second sentence, and move it to the first sentence.

1. Leaders of the colonies met in Philadelphia. There were thirteen colonies.

_____

2. Ben Franklin was a member of the group. He was respected.

_____

3. They met in a room in the State House. The room was stuffy.

_____

4. The colonists accepted the Declaration of Independence after days of talks. The talks lasted three days.

_____

5. John Hancock wrote his signature. His signature was bold.

_____

6. Ben Franklin encouraged the men to stay united. The men were brave.

_____

**Go back to the sentences you wrote.
Circle the adjectives that you moved.**

Lesson 27: *A, An, The*

LEARN

The words *a*, *an*, and *the* are special adjectives called **articles**.

- Use *a* before a singular noun that begins with a consonant sound.

  What do you call **a** man who doesn't sink?

- Use *an* before a singular noun that begins with a vowel sound.

  How do you know when there is **an** elephant under your bed?

- Use *the* before both singular and plural nouns.
  Why did **the** pony cough?
  I love **the** jokes in this book!

PRACTICE

A For each noun, write the singular form with *a* or *an* in the first column Write the singular form with **the** in the second column. Write the plural form with **the** in the third column. The first one is done for you.

	With **a or an** *(singular)*	**With** **the** *(singular)*	**With** **the** *(plural)*
1. owl	an owl	the owl	the owls
2. pony			
3. orange			
4. ribbon			
5. egg			

	With a or an *(singular)*	With the *(singular)*	With the *(plural)*
6. brush	_____	_____	_____
7. apple	_____	_____	_____
8. tooth	_____	_____	_____
9. patch	_____	_____	_____
10. insect	_____	_____	_____

B *Underline the article in ( ) that correctly completes each sentence.*

1. What is gray, has four legs, and (a, an) trunk?

2. It's (a, an) mouse on vacation.

3. Why did (an, the) turkey cross the road twice?

4. He wanted to prove he wasn't (a, an) chicken.

5. How do you change (a, an) eggplant into another vegetable?

6. Throw it up in (a, the) air, and it will come down squash.

7. Why are (the, a) legs of (a, an) ostrich so long?

8. They have to be long to touch (the, an) ground.

9. Where can you find (a, an) ocean with no water?

10. The ocean is on (a, an) map!

11. Why did (an, the) pig want to become (a, an) actor?

12. He was (a, an) ham!

C *A group of students wrote their favorite riddles and answers. They made five mistakes using articles. Find the mistakes, and use the proofreading marks to correct them.*

Our Favorite Jokes and Riddles

Proofreading Marks

∧	Add
⊙	Period
ℓ	Take out
≡	Capital letter
/	Small letter

1. **Riddle** Why did the chicken cross the playground?

   Answer to get to the other slide

2. **Riddle** Why do a birds fly south in the winter?

   Answer It's too far to walk.

3. **Riddle** What clothing does a house wear?

   Answer a address

4. **Riddle** Why was the cook put in jail?

   Answer He beat up a egg.

5. **Riddle** How do you find a lost rabbit?

   Answer Make a noise like an carrot.

6. **Riddle** What begins with an e and ends with an e, but has only one letter in it?

   Answer a envelope

Look Back Did you fix five articles?

Write Your Own

WRITE

D *Make up a few riddles about familiar things. Use an article in the answer to each of your riddles. Here are a few to get you started.*

Riddle What has six legs and two heads but walks on four feet?

Answer a rider on a horse

Riddle What grows down in the middle of winter?

Answer an icicle

1. Riddle _____

_____

Answer _____

2. Riddle _____

_____

Answer _____

3. Riddle _____

_____

Answer _____

Notice that the answers to the riddles are not complete sentences. In informal writing, such as this riddle activity, it is acceptable to give your answers as phrases.

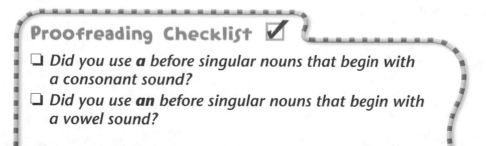

Proofreading Checklist ✓

❑ *Did you use **a** before singular nouns that begin with a consonant sound?*

❑ *Did you use **an** before singular nouns that begin with a vowel sound?*

Lesson 28: **Comparing with Adjectives**

LEARN

Adjectives can be used to compare.
Adjectives that compare tell how people,
places, or things are alike or different.

Mount Everest

- **To compare two people, places, or things,
  add -*er* to most adjectives.**
    Mount McKinley (or Denali) in Alaska is
    higher than Mount Whitney in California.

- **To compare more than two people, places,
  or things, add -*est* to most adjectives.**
    Mount Everest is the **highest** mountain
    in the world.

PRACTICE

A *Write the adjective in ( ) that correctly completes each sentence.*

1. The blue whale is _____ than the howler monkey.
(louder, loudest)

2. The blue whale is the _____ animal of all.
(louder, loudest)

3. The Arctic Ocean is the _____ ocean in the world.
(smaller, smallest)

4. The Caribbean Sea is _____ than the Gulf of Mexico.
(deeper, deepest)

5. The Pacific Ocean is the _____ ocean of all.
(deeper, deepest)

6. London's Underground is the _____ train tunnel
anywhere. (longer, longest)

7. Mammoth Cave in Kentucky is _____ than London's Underground. (longer, longest)

8. The Sahara Desert in Africa has the world's _____ sand dunes. (taller, tallest)

9. Those dunes are _____ than the Empire State Building. (taller, tallest)

10. The _____ point in the Empire State Building is the top of the tower. (higher, highest)

B *Write the form of the adjective in ( ) that correctly completes each sentence.*

1. Fairlawn is the _____ town in our county. (great)

2. The Wilson House is the _____ building in Fairlawn. (old)

3. Fairlawn Elementary School has the _____ students of all the schools in the county. (smart)

4. Our park is _____ than the park in Bingham. (new)

5. Our park has the _____ hill for sledding. (steep)

6. We are having the _____ winter in our town's history. (warm)

7. The sledding season will be _____ this year than last year. (short)

8. The new paths in the park are _____ than the old ones. (smooth)

9. The old gravel path is the _____ of all the paths. (rough)

10. I can skate _____ on the new paths than on the old ones. (fast)

Sonja wrote about her day at a swim meet. She made seven mistakes when comparing with adjectives. Find the mistakes, and use the proofreading marks to correct them.

Remember

Add *-er* to most adjectives to compare two people, places, or things.

Add *-est* to compare more than two.

The sky is the brighter blue of any day this week. The big day has finally arrived. Today is the school's first swim meet.

Jay is the youngest of my three friends, and he is the shorter, too. He is the harder to find in the crowd anywhere. I am always the one to call out his name because I have the loudest voice.

My friend Joan is calmest than I am. She says, "Don't worry. We'll find Jay." She's right. We finally find Jay, and we take our seats near our team's bench.

My friend Ted is a strongest swimmer than I am. He is the fastest swimmer of all at the swim meet. He wins his race! I am proudest of him than ever!

It is late, and the sky is darkest now than it was before. Rain clouds are gathering, too. After an exciting day, it's time to go home.

Proofreading Marks

∧ Add
⊙ Period
ℒ Take out
≡ Capital letter
/ Small letter

Did you fix seven adjectives that compare?

Write Your Own

WRITE

 Additional Resources at
grammarworkshop.com

D Write some facts comparing people, places, or things in your
neighborhood. Use four adjectives from each box in your
facts. Check a dictionary if you need help spelling a word.

higher	longer
quieter	sweeter
older	taller

highest	longest
quietest	sweetest
oldest	tallest

1. _____

_____

_____

2. _____

_____

_____

3. _____

_____

_____

4. _____

_____

_____

Proofreading Checklist ✓

❏ *Did you use the* **-er** *ending to compare two people,
places, or things?*

❏ *Did you use the* **-est** *ending to compare more
than two?*

Lesson 29: More Comparing with Adjectives

LEARN

Most adjectives that compare two end in *-er*. Most adjectives that compare three or more end in *-est*.

Sometimes you need to make spelling changes before adding *-er* or *-est*.

- If an adjective ends in e, drop the *e* before adding *-er* or *-est*.

    wide + er = wid**er**   wide + est = wid**est**

- If an adjective ends in a consonant and *y*, change the *y* to *i* before adding *-er* or *-est*.

    tiny + er = tin**ier**   tiny + est = tin**iest**

- If an adjective ends in one vowel followed by a consonant, double the consonant before adding *-er* or *-est*.

    fat + er = fat**ter**   fat + est = fat**test**

PRACTICE

A *In Column A, add **-er** to each adjective. In Column B, add **-est** to each adjective. Remember to make the necessary spelling changes before adding **-er** and **-est**.*

	A	B
1. wet	_____	_____
2. hungry	_____	_____
3. happy	_____	_____
4. safe	_____	_____
5. sad	_____	_____
6. pretty	_____	_____

	A	**B**
7. slim	_____	_____
8. brave	_____	_____
9. flat	_____	_____
10. blue	_____	_____

B Write the form of the adjective in ( ) that correctly completes each sentence.

1. This animal park is the _____ in the country. (big)

2. Saturday is the _____ day of the week at the park. (busy)

3. The ostrich is the _____ bird in the world. (large)

4. The chimps are _____ than the gorillas. (cute)

5. Chimps do _____ things than gorillas do. (silly)

6. The snake room is _____ than the monkey house. (hot)

7. Is this elephant _____ than that rhinoceros? (heavy)

8. The female lion looks _____ than the male lion. (tame)

9. Are owls really _____ than other birds? (wise)

10. The _____ animals of all were the koalas. (sleepy)

11. The _____ thing of all was the giraffe's 18-inch long tongue! (strange)

12. This is the _____ animal park of all! (fine)

C Two students wrote about their favorite animals in an animal park. They made six mistakes using adjectives that compare. Find the mistakes, and use the proofreading marks to fix them.

Sam Cole

The park has six wolves. The white wolf is the thinner in the whole group. The red wolf has the prettier face, and I like that wolf the best. I heard the wolves howl and growl. The growling was scaryest than the howling.

Proofreading Marks

∧   Add
⊙   Period
𝒆   Take out
≡   Capital letter
/   Small letter

Kim Pak

I think the langurs are the niceer monkeys in the park. The larger of the five langurs climbed to the highest branch in a tree. He was also the noisyer one of the group. He shouted down at everyone from high in the tree.

Did you fix six adjectives that compare?

Langur

Write Your Own

WRITE

D In each item, use the adjective shown to write two sentences that compare the animals in the picture. In the first sentence, use the adjective to compare two animals. In the second sentence, use the adjective to compare three animals.

Elephant   Parrot   Emu

1. heavy _____

_____

_____

2. big _____

_____

_____

3. cute _____

_____

_____

Proofreading Checklist ☑

❏ Did you use the **-er** ending to compare two animals?
❏ Did you use the **-est** ending to compare three animals?
❏ Did you make the necessary spelling changes when adding the endings?

Lesson 30: **Comparing with *More* and *Most***

LEARN

■ **Most adjectives with two or more syllables need the words *more* or *most* to compare.**

- **Use *more* with an adjective to compare two people, places, or things.**
  Fruit is **more popular** than nuts at our school.

- **Use *most* with an adjective to compare more than two people, places, or things.**
  Popcorn is the **most popular** snack of all.

■ **Avoid the common errors below.**

- **Do not use *-er* or *-est* with an adjective when you should use *more* or *most*.**
  INCORRECT Lunch was **deliciouser** than supper.
  CORRECT Lunch was **more delicious** than supper.

- **Do not add *-er* or *-est* to an adjective when you use *more* or *most*.**
  INCORRECT Breakfast is the **most importantest** meal of all.
  CORRECT Breakfast is the **most important** meal of all.

PRACTICE

A *Each adjective below contains two or more syllables. In Column A, use* **more** *with each adjective. In Column B, use* **most** *with each adjective.*

	A	*B*
1. eager	_____	_____
2. exciting	_____	_____
3. tired	_____	_____
4. helpful	_____	_____

	A	B
5. unusual	_____	_____
6. difficult	_____	_____
7. active	_____	_____
8. welcome	_____	_____
9. surprised	_____	_____
10. enjoyable	_____	_____

B Write **more** or **most** to complete each sentence.

1. Cereal is _____ interesting with fruit than without it.

2. The chicken is _____ tender than the steak.

3. A pasta salad is _____ filling than a green salad.

4. A salad with carrots and tomatoes is _____ colorful than a salad with just lettuce

5. Hot drinks are _____ comforting than cold drinks.

6. Blueberries are the _____ plentiful in summer.

7. Berries are _____ expensive in winter than in summer.

8. The restaurant is _____ crowded at noon than at any other time.

9. The restaurant has the _____ pleasant view of the river.

10. Holiday dinners are the _____ delicious meals of the year!

C *Mr. Li's students wrote down their questions and answers from a talk with a school cafeteria worker. The students made five mistakes when they used* **more** *and* **most** *to compare. Find the mistakes, and correct them. Use the proofreading marks in the box.*

Q: What is the most popularest fruit among students?

A: Apples win that contest. Red delicious apples seem to be more popularer than Granny Smith apples.

Q: Have you thought about having a salad bar?

A: That's the most interesting idea I've heard!

Q: Are tacos most filling than pizza?

A: They can be. It depends on what is in the taco or on the pizza.

Q: Why do you serve chicken more often than hamburgers?

A: We find that chicken is most popular than beef.

Q: Which drink is the more delicious of all?

A: That would be the fruit shakes.

Proofreading Marks

∧	Add
⊙	Period
℘	Take out
≡	Capital letter
/	Small letter

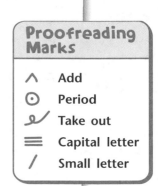

Did you correct five mistakes with the use of *more* and *most*?

Write Your Own

WRITE

D List your favorite for each item below. Then write a sentence
that compares this favorite to similar foods. Try to use **more**
and **most** with adjectives to compare each favorite to another food.
The first one is done for you.

1. My Favorite Fruit _strawberries_____

Strawberries are the most colorful fruit of all.

_____

2. My Favorite Vegetable _____

_____

_____

3. My Favorite Sandwich _____

_____

_____

4. My Favorite Soup _____

_____

_____

5. My Favorite Drink _____

_____

_____

Proofreading Checklist ✓

❏ *Did you use **more** or an adjective with the -er ending
to compare two things?*

❏ *Did you use **most** or an adjective with the -est ending
to compare more than two?*

Lesson 31: **Adverbs**

LEARN

An **adverb** is a word that generally describes, or tells about, a verb. Adverbs tell *how, when,* or *where* an action happens. They can come before or after the verbs they describe.

HOW	The lions hunted **silently**.
WHEN	**Then** one female lion leaped.
WHERE	The antelopes ran **away**.

- **Most adverbs that tell *how* end in *-ly*.**
  quickly   easily   sadly   strongly

- **Here are some adverbs that tell *when*.**
  always   often   then   first   soon   yesterday

- **Here are some adverbs that tell *where*.**
  inside   outside   here   there   uphill   everywhere

PRACTICE

A *Underline the adverb that describes the verb in **dark print**. Then circle the words that tell what the adverb does.*

1. Yesterday we **visited** a safari park.   *tells how*   *tells when*

2. We **saw** several big cats there.   *tells when*   *tells where*

3. Cats **vary** widely in size.   *tells how*   *tells where*

4. All cats **move** gracefully.   *tells when*   *tells how*

5. Two cats **raced** uphill.   *tells when*   *tells where*

6. Cats **run** silently on padded feet.   *tells how*   *tells where*

7. A cat's sharp eyes **see** far.   *tells when*   *tells where*

8. Their keen noses soon **notice** a smell.   *tells when*   *tells where*

9. Their sharp teeth **cut** deeply. *tells how* *tells where*

10. These lean hunters often **hunt** smaller animals. *tells how* *tells when*

B *Find and underline the adverb in each sentence. Then write the adverb and the verb it describes on the lines. The first one is done for you.*

	Adverb	Verb
1. Lions <u>usually</u> live in family groups.	usually	live
2. Other big cats live alone.		
3. Female cats always stay with their cubs.		
4. Cubs watch their mothers carefully.		
5. Soon they learn to hunt.		
6. Many tigers once lived in Asia.		
7. Leopards climb trees swiftly.		
8. These cats mostly hunt at night.		
9. The number of big cats fell recently.		
10. Animal parks now guard big cats.		

C Write an adverb to complete each sentence. Choose an adverb from the box, or use an adverb of your own.

always	finally	loudly	nearby
never	proudly	slowly	then

A group of mice _____ feared a big cat.
(1)

This cat, which lived _____, chased and tried
(2)

to catch them. _____, a young mouse decided
(3)

what to do about it.

"Let's hang a bell around the cat's neck," this mouse

said _____. "That way, we'll hear the cat
(4)

whenever she comes around."

The other mice clapped _____. They had
(5)

_____ heard such a good idea!
(6)

_____ an old mouse stood up. _____
(7)   (8)

he turned to the mice. "A bell on the cat would certainly

make us safer," he agreed. "But I have one question.

Who puts the bell on the cat?"

WRITE

Adverbs tell *how*, *when*, and *where* something happens.
You can tell more about the verb in your sentence by
adding an adverb.

We talked about the story.
We talked **excitedly** about the story.

 D *Add an adverb to each sentence. Choose an adverb from the box,
or use an adverb of your own. Write the revised sentence on the line.*

> always   downstairs   everywhere
> inside   noisily   lazily   patiently

1. My cat Ginger wakes up when I do. _____

_____

2. She follows me. _____

_____

3. She sniffs. _____

_____

4. Then she meows. _____

_____

5. I feed her, and she settles down. _____

_____

6. She stays by the window. _____

_____

7. She waits. _____

_____

Lesson 32: **Comparing With Adverbs**

LEARN

- An **adverb** is a word that generally describes an action verb. It can tell *how*, *when*, or *where* an action happens.

- You can use adverbs to compare two or more actions.

    At the state fair, my horse ran **fast**.
    Sheila's horse ran **faster** than my horse.
    Karen's horse ran **fastest** of all.

Add -*er* to most one-syllable adverbs to compare two actions.

Add -*est* to most one-syllable adverbs to compare more than two actions.

PRACTICE

A *Write the adverb in ( ) that correctly completes each sentence.*

1. The state fair seemed to come _____ this year than it did last year! (sooner, soonest)

2. Of all the contestants, my brother Sal worked _____ to grow sunflowers for the plant show. (harder, hardest)

3. His sunflower bloomed _____ than mine. (earlier, earliest)

4. Sal's sunflower scored _____ of all the flowers in the show. (higher, highest)

5. We cheered _____ of any family for the contestants. (louder, loudest)

6. I prepared _____ for the horse competition than for the plant show. (harder, hardest)

7. I practiced _____ on my jumps than my competitors did. (longer, longest)

8. My horse Chelsea jumped _____ than she did last year. (higher, highest)

9. In fact, she leaped _____ of all the horses in her group. (higher, highest)

10. She ran _____ than she ran last year, too. (faster, fastest)

 Write the form of the adverb in ( ) that correctly completes each sentence. Think about how many actions are being compared.

1. This morning, I waited (long) than usual for my brother.   _____

2. He usually arrives at the show area (late) than I do.   _____

3. Before breakfast, I noticed that our cow Belle was moving (slow) than usual.   _____

4. Usually, Belle walks (fast) of all the cows in the pen.   _____

5. Today, she walked (slow) of all.   _____

6. She held her head (low) than the other cows did.   _____

7. I thought (hard) than ever about what to do.   _____

8. Belle nudged (close) to me when she noticed the handful of hay.   _____

9. She started to moo (loud) than before.   _____

10. She held her head (high), too.   _____

11. She licked my hand (fast) than she had ever done.   _____

12. Belle pulled on the rope (hard) of all the cows once she'd had a snack.   _____

C Carl wrote this e-mail to his father to tell him how their animals did at the fair. He made five mistakes when using adverbs that compare. Find the mistakes, and use the proofreading marks to correct them.

Dear Dad,

We were so proud of our animals. They scored highest than they've ever scored at the fair! The horses did really well. Jingles ran fastest than Shadow, but both horses won ribbons. Of all the horses, Shadow ran closer to Jingles.

The rabbits won two ribbons as well. Buttercup hopped out of her cage slowest than Milky Way did, but she looked beautiful and won the ribbon. Milky Way nibbled the judge's finger hardest than he nibbled his juicy carrot! He won a ribbon anyway though, because he hopped higher than last year's champion.

It was a great day for Lazy R Ranch. I can't wait to show you all the ribbons!

Love,

Carl

Proofreading Marks

∧	Add
⊙	Period
℘	Take out
≡	Capital letter
/	Small letter

LOOK Back Did you correct five mistakes with adverbs that compare?

Write Your Own

WRITE

D *Imagine you are attending a state fair or competition. Use the words in ( ) to help you describe what you saw. You can use a dictionary to help you spell words.*

1. (slower) _____

2. (lower) _____

3. (highest) _____

4. (fastest) _____

5. (longer) _____

6. (sooner) _____

7. (closest) _____

8. (hardest) _____

Imagine that you are talking to your friend about a state fair or competition. How would the language you use in speaking be different from the language you would use in writing a report about the state fair or competition?

_____

_____

_____

_____

Proofreading Checklist ✔

❑ *Did you use -**er** to compare two actions?*
❑ *Did you use -**est** to compare more than two actions?*

Lesson 33: Negatives

LEARN

■ A **negative** is a word that means "no." The words *not, nobody, nothing, nowhere,* and *never* are negatives. The words *don't, won't,* and other contractions made with *not* are also negatives.

> You are **not** alone.
> **Don't** give up hope!

■ Do not use two negatives together in one sentence. To correct a sentence with a double negative, take out one negative or replace it with a word such as *any, ever, anything, anywhere,* or *anyone.*

INCORRECT	I **don't** want **no** advice.
CORRECT	I **don't** want advice.
	I **don't** want **any** advice.
INCORRECT	I **don't never** give up hope.
CORRECT	I **don't** give up hope.
	I **don't ever** give up hope.

*don't
won't
never
no
not
nobody
nothing
nowhere*

PRACTICE

A *Write the negative word in each sentence.*

1. Money doesn't grow on trees. _____

2. Winners never quit. _____

3. There is no time like the present. _____

4. Don't give up the ship! _____

5. You can lead a horse to water, but you can't make it drink. _____

6. We have nowhere to go but up. _____

7. That's not fair! _____

8. Rome wasn't built in a day. _____

9. Do you promise to tell the truth, the whole truth,
and nothing but the truth? _____

10. Nobody knows the trouble I've seen. _____

B *Write the word in ( ) that correctly completes each sentence.*

1. There isn't _____ new under the sun.
(nothing, anything)

2. There _____ no place like home. (is, isn't)

3. I cannot tell _____ lie. (no, a)

4. Don't _____ put off until tomorrow what you
can do today. (ever, never)

5. We _____ nothing to fear but fear itself.
(have, haven't)

6. There was nothing _____ could do to help.
(anybody, nobody)

7. Nobody said life _____ be easy. (would, wouldn't)

8. Don't expect _____ for free. (anything, nothing)

9. There _____ no business like show business.
(is, isn't)

10. You haven't seen _____ yet. (anything, nothing)

C *Read this advice column from a school newspaper. The writers used five double negatives in their writing. Look for the mistakes, and correct them. Use the proofreading marks in the box.*

Ask Mr. Tips

Dear Mr. Tips,

I hate tests! I don't never do well on them. I study for them, but I start to sweat once a test begins. Suddenly, the questions don't make no sense. What's wrong with me?

Barely Passing

Dear Barely Passing,

There isn't nothing wrong with you. You just need to relax. Breathe deeply before a test. Tell yourself that you will do well. Don't pay attention to nobody in the room. If you can't answer a question, that's okay. Go on to the next one, and don't think nothing about it.

Mr. Tips

Proofreading Marks

∧	Add
⊙	Period
ℰ	Take out
☰	Capital letter
/	Small letter

LOOK Back

Did you correct five double negatives?

Write Your Own

WRITE

D *Now it is time to give yourself some advice. First tell about a problem that has been bothering you lately. Then write a few sentences of advice. Tell yourself what you think you should do to solve the problem. Use some negative words in your writing.*

My Problem

_____

_____

_____

My Advice to Myself

_____

_____

_____

_____

_____

_____

_____

_____

_____

_____

Proofreading Checklist ☑

❏ *Did you use negative words correctly in your sentences?*

Unit 4 Review
Lessons 26–33

Adjectives (pp. 120–127) *Underline the adjectives in each sentence. Remember that articles are adjectives, too.*

1. We love the funny cartoons.

2. They can tell an interesting story.

3. The drawings are simple.

4. Many cartoons appear in the local newspaper.

5. A favorite artist is Charles Schulz.

Comparing with Adjectives (pp. 128–135) *Write the form of the adjective in ( ) that correctly completes each sentence.*

6. This comic strip is (long) than the other one. _____

7. The (funny) line in a comic strip comes at the end. _____

8. Some comic strips are (silly) than others. _____

9. The characters often look (strange) than real people. _____

10. *Little Orphan Annie* is the (old) comic strip in our newspaper. _____

Comparing with *More* and *Most* (pp. 136–139)
*Write **more** or **most** to complete each sentence.*

11. Drawings are _____ important than words in most cartoons.

12. This newspaper has the _____ cartoons of all.

13. This artist uses _____ speech balloons than the other artists.

14. These cartoon characters are _____ interesting than those.

15. These drawings are the _____ beautiful art in the book.

Adverbs (pp. 140–143) *Underline the adverb in each sentence.*

16. I read the comics in the newspaper today.

17. Many comic strips are printed there.

18. Soon I will read them.

19. I glanced at them quickly.

20. The drawings always tell a story.

Comparing with Adverbs (pp. 144–147) *Write the form of the adverb in ( ) that correctly completes each sentence.*

21. This cartoonist ranks (high) of all the artists. _____

22. She worked (hard) than usual last week. _____

23. Her work arrived (soon) than I expected. _____

24. We cheered (loud) of all when the strip hit the presses. _____

25. Of all the projects, this is the one we worked (long) on. _____

Negatives (pp. 148–151) *Underline the word in ( ) that correctly completes each sentence.*

26. I haven't (ever, never) seen such a funny cartoon.

27. There isn't (anything, nothing) funnier than this drawing!

28. You don't need (no, any) words to understand the meaning of this cartoon.

29. I don't (never, ever) look at black-and-white cartoons.

30. There (is, isn't) nothing like colorful cartoons.

Unit 4 Test

DIRECTIONS *Fill in the circle next to the sentence that shows the correct spelling and use of adjectives, adverbs, and negatives.*

1. ○ A pond is smaller than a lake.
   ○ You won't never see a more beautiful place than Echo Park.
   ○ Echo Pond is the prettyest pond in the park.
   ○ Canada geese are the most commonest of the birds here.

2. ○ Echo Pond is more popularer now than five years ago.
   ○ The water is more cleaner now than in the past.
   ○ There aren't no big boats on it.
   ○ This is the most important area for watching birds.

3. ○ A duck is smaller than an goose.
   ○ That swan is the bigest bird.
   ○ Of all the birds here, which flies faster?
   ○ The swans are more beautiful than the geese.

4. ○ A otter lives on the pond.
   ○ That's the deepest part of all.
   ○ This is the noisyest bullfrog.
   ○ The bullfrog is the most largest of all American frogs.

5. ○ Summer heat makes a water lilies grow.
   ○ I paddled in a canoe yesterday.
   ○ I never enjoyed nothing more.
   ○ We went out on the hotest day.

6. ○ A snake wasn't doing nothing.
   ○ The ducks swam lazily in the pond.
   ○ The beavers were making a more bigger lodge.
   ○ A hawk soared higher than an pelican.

7. ○ Autumn is a more difficult time for lake animals than summer.
   ○ Food is more scarcer in cold weather than in warm weather.
   ○ The geese don't never stay past October.
   ○ Life is more harder here than in other places.

8. ○ The frogs do not go nowhere.
   ○ An beaver sleeps most of winter.
   ○ The more warmer days of spring will be here soon.
   ○ I'll be here to see the ice melt.

DIRECTIONS *Read the paragraphs, and look carefully at each underlined part. Fill in the circle next to the answer choice that shows the correct use and spelling of adjectives, adverbs, and negatives. If the underlined part is already correct, fill in the circle for "Correct as is."*

It was an October day, <u>and it was colder</u> than usual for autumn. We were
(9)
canoeing on Echo Pond. The winds <u>were blowing harder now</u> than they were
(10)
an hour ago. My uncle paddled as fast as he could. That's when his paddle
broke in half and floated away. <u>There wasn't nothing</u> we could do.
(11)
We wanted to shout for help, but <u>we couldn't see nobody</u>. <u>The weather</u>
(12)   (13)
<u>got fierceer</u>. Luckily, the wind changed direction and blew us safely back
(13)
to shore. It was <u>a afternoon I won't never</u> forget.
(14)

9. ○ and it was most cold
○ and it was coldest
○ and it was more colder
○ Correct as is

10. ○ were blowing hardest now
○ were blowing hard now
○ were blowing more harder now
○ Correct as is

11. ○ There was nothing
○ There wasn't not anything
○ There was anything
○ Correct as is

12. ○ we couldn't see no one
○ we couldn't see anyone
○ we could not see nobody
○ Correct as is

13. ○ The weather got more fiercer.
○ The weather got most fiercest.
○ The weather got fiercer.
○ Correct as is

14. ○ a afternoon I won't ever
○ the afternoon I won't never
○ an afternoon I won't ever
○ Correct as is

Lesson 34: **Subject Pronouns**

LEARN

■ A **pronoun** is a word that takes the place of one or more nouns.

■ A **subject pronoun** takes the place of the noun or nouns in the subject. It is used as the subject of a sentence.

Mary had a little lamb.
She had a little lamb.

Jack and Jill went up the hill.
They went up the hill.

The spider made a web.
It made a web.

Dad and I love nursery rhymes.
We love nursery rhymes.

■ These are the subject pronouns. The pronoun *you* can be singular or plural.

SINGULAR	I	you	he	she	it
PLURAL	we	you	they		

The pronoun *I* is always capitalized.

PRACTICE

A *Write the subject pronoun in each sentence.*

1. We read the rhymes of Mother Goose. _____

2. They tell about familiar characters. _____

3. I like the rhyme about Jack and Jill. _____

4. It may be 1000 years old! _____

5. You probably have heard of Old King Cole. _____

6. Long ago, he was a king in England. _____

7. I found information about Mother Goose. _____

8. She may have collected these rhymes in France long ago. _____

9. They were passed on to other storytellers. _____

10. We may never know for sure who Mother Goose was. _____

B *Replace the word or words in **dark print** with a subject pronoun. The first one is done for you.*

1. You and I look for some rhymes. _____We_____

2. Tom and Pat read some of their favorites. _____

3. Little Jack Horner sat in a corner. _____

4. Old Mother Hubbard went to her cupboard. _____

5. Little boys should be asleep when the moon begins to peep. _____

6. The north wind will blow, and we will have snow. _____

7. London Bridge is falling down. _____

8. Three blind mice ran after the farmer's wife. _____

9. Little Bo Peep lost her sheep. _____

10. Little Tommy Tittlemouse lived in a little house. _____

C *Here is a message from Terry. She pretends to visit the land of Mother Goose. Write a subject pronoun from the box to complete each sentence. You will use some pronouns more than once.*

he	I	it	she	they	we	you

I have good news! _____ have just visited the (1)

land of Mother Goose. _____ will be happy to (2)

hear that things are much better there!

For one thing, Jack and Jill now have a sink in their

house. Now _____ don't have to go up that (3)

hill for water. Jack's head also feels much better.

_____ had hurt it falling down the hill. (4)

Old Mother Hubbard is doing well, too. At one time,

_____ was sad because her cupboard was bare. (5)

Now there's a new supermarket across the street.

Finally, _____ visited the old lady who lived (6)

in a shoe. At one time, _____ had so many (7)

children she didn't know what to do. Now _____ (8)

all live in a six-bedroom house. _____ has a big (9)

yard. The children said, "_____ love it here!" (10)

Revising Sentences

WRITE

 Additional Resources at grammarworkshop.com

If you repeat the same subject over and over, your sentences will sound boring.

> **The men** tried to help Humpty Dumpty.
> **The men** rode quickly to the wall.

Replace the overused subject in the second sentence with a subject pronoun.

> The men tried to help Humpty Dumpty.
> **They** rode quickly to the wall.

D *Rewrite the second sentence in each pair. Use a subject pronoun to replace the overused subject.*

1. Humpty Dumpty had a great fall. Humpty Dumpty could not be put together again.

_____

2. Super Glue was invented. Super Glue put Humpty Dumpty together again.

_____

3. The Fair Lady heard about Super Glue. The Fair Lady used the glue on London Bridge.

_____

4. London Bridge was falling down. London Bridge is fine now.

_____

5. Little Bo Peep's sheep always got lost. Little Bo Peep's sheep now wear loud bells.

_____

6. The spider was washed out of a rain spout. The spider climbs only on sunny days now.

_____

Lesson 35: Pronoun-Verb Agreement

LEARN

A present-tense verb must agree with the subject pronoun.

- When the subject pronoun is *he, she,* or *it,* add *-s* or *-es* to the verb.

     He prepares the clay.
     She pinches it into a pot.
     It dries in the sun.

     Remember to change the *y* to *i* before adding *-es.*

- When the subject pronoun is *I, we, you,* or *they,* do not add *-s* or *-es* to the verb.

     I roll the clay.
     We stretch it out.
     You mold it into a vase.
     They carry it to the table.

PRACTICE

A *Write the verb in ( ) that correctly completes each sentence.*

1. This week we _____ pottery in art class. (makes, make)

2. I _____ our teacher Mrs. Diaz carefully. (watches, watch)

3. She _____ clay for the students. (mixes, mix)

4. They _____ the clay into long coils. (rolls, roll)

5. "You _____ bowls from these coils," Mrs. Diaz explains. (forms, form)

6. First, Andy _____ the coils on top of each other. (stacks, stack)

7. Together, they _____ down on the coils. (presses, press)

8. Then he _____ it by himself. (tries, try)

9. It really _____ like a bowl! (looks, look)

10. Andy _____ for more clay. (wishes, wish)

B *Write the form of the verb in ( ) that correctly completes each sentence.*

1. He _____ a pattern on his bowl. (scratch)

2. She _____ handles to the bowl. (add)

3. Then we _____ our bowls in the sun. (put)

4. They _____ two days to dry. (take)

5. On Thursday, Mrs. Diaz _____ us more. (teach)

6. She _____ her bowl with a special stone. (polish)

7. Then she _____ it with paint. (decorate)

8. She _____ three different colors. (use)

9. I _____ designs on my bowls, too. (paint)

10. They _____ overnight. (dry)

11. We _____ our pottery proudly. (display)

12. "What beautiful bowls!" Mrs. Diaz

_____ . (cry)

Mike made eight mistakes in pronoun-verb agreement in this description. Use the proofreading marks to correct the errors.

Today, Mrs. Diaz shows us a potter's wheel. She place a wet round lump of clay in the center of this wheel. It turn slowly, and she push her thumbs down into the middle of the clay. She makes a hole that is called a well. It becomes the opening of the pot.

The wheel spins faster now. Mrs. Diaz's fingers run over the pot. Slowly they squeezes up the clay to form the sides of the pot. She watch the clay carefully. The sides have to be even all around.

Next, Mrs. Diaz takes out a sponge. She finish off the rim of the pot with the sponge. It look really neat and smooth.

Finally, she scrape the bottom of the pot with a sharp stick to clean it. When it dries in a day or two, she will bake it in a kiln.

Proofreading Marks

∧	Add
⊙	Period
ℓ	Take out
≡	Capital letter
/	Small letter

Did you correct eight mistakes in pronoun-verb agreement?

WRITE

Additional Resources at
grammarworkshop.com

D *Complete the second sentence in each pair. Use the subject pronoun and a present-tense verb to tell what happens next. Be sure the verb agrees with the subject pronoun.*

1. Denny gets more clay. He _____

_____

2. My brothers make flowerpots. They _____

_____

3. Terry and I use the potter's wheel. We _____

_____

4. Lucy makes a toy house from clay. She _____

_____

5. Chad paints a crazy design on his pot. He _____

_____

6. Edward makes a vase. He _____

_____

7. Chad wants to make something new. He _____

_____

8. Lucy's toy house is dry now. She _____

_____

Proofreading Checklist ✓

❏ *Did you make the verbs agree with the subject pronouns?*
❏ *Did you end each sentence with the correct end mark?*

Lesson 36: **Object Pronouns**

LEARN

- An **object pronoun** takes the place of a noun that follows an action verb.

  I found **Jack**
  I found **him**.

An object pronoun also follows a word such as *to, for, by,* and *with*.

  I hid with **Jack**.
  I hid with **him**.
  Sheila hid by **Jack and me**.
  Sheila hid by **us**.

- These are the object pronouns.
  The pronoun *you* can be singular or plural.

SINGULAR	me	you	him	her	it
PLURAL	us	you	them		

PRACTICE

A *Write the object pronoun in each sentence.*

1. My friends played hide-and-seek with me. _____

2. I told them to hide first. _____

3. "I will wait for you to hide," I said. _____

4. Amanda hid behind a tree, but I spotted her. _____

5. She ran for home, but I got to it first. _____

6. Jack sneezed in the bushes, so I caught him next. _____

7. "You have to free us!" they called to Sheila. _____

8. I couldn't find her anywhere. _____

9. Suddenly, she ran by me and freed the others. _____

10. I had to find them all again. _____

B *Rewrite each sentence. Replace the word or words in **dark print** with an object pronoun.*

1. My name is Don, and I like to play tag with **my friends**. _____

_____

2. "Don, you're it!" they say to **Don**. _____

_____

3. Jack and Sheila shout, "Don, try and catch **Jack and Sheila**!" _____

_____

4. Jack is a fast runner, but I can usually catch **Jack**. _____

_____

5. Sheila darts in and out, but I can tag **Sheila**. _____

_____

6. We love tag, and sometimes we play **tag** with a foam rubber ball.

_____

7. "Try not to get hit by **the ball**," I say. _____

_____

8. Devon showed **Jack, Sheila, and me** how to play. _____

_____

C *Write an object pronoun to complete each sentence. Choose an object pronoun from the box. You will use some pronouns more than once.*

| her | him | it | me | them | us | you |

Yesterday, my friends were at my house. My mother taught _____ a new game called
(1)
Sardines. Mom said, "My parents taught _____
(2)
this game when I was little." The game sounded like fun.
Here's how we played _____.
(3)
We all closed our eyes while Devon ran and hid.
Then each person went out alone to find _____.
(4)
Sheila found Devon first. He was hiding behind the garage. Sheila hid there with _____. Next,
(5)
I found _____ hiding with Devon. I hid with
(6)
_____, too. Soon Jack found _____
(7)   (8)
behind the garage. He hid with us, too. We were all crammed in together like sardines in a can!
Finally, Amanda found _____. She was
(9)
the last person playing, so the game was over.
Mom said, "I watched _____ play. You
(10)
did very well for your first time as sardines!"

WRITE

If you use the same nouns over and over again, your sentences will sound dull.

> **Devon and Cathy** hid behind the fence. I found **Devon and Cathy** there.

In the second sentence above, you can replace the overused words with an object pronoun. Then your writing will sound better.

> Devon and Cathy hid behind the fence. I found **them** there.

 *Rewrite the second sentence in each pair. Replace the overused word or words in **dark print** with an object pronoun.*

1. Jack wanted to play tag. Sheila and I played with **Jack**.

_____

2. That maple tree is home base. Touch **that maple tree**, and you're free.

_____

3. I know I tagged Sheila. Jack said I missed **Sheila**.

_____

4. "You'll never catch Sheila and me," Jack said. "You'll never catch **Sheila and me**." _____

5. I finally tagged all the players. I told **all the players** that I had won.

_____

6. Some other friends wanted to play Sardines. I showed **my other friends** how to play. _____

7. "Sardines is like backwards hide-and-seek," said Chris. "I like to play **Sardines**." _____

Lesson 37: Using *I* and *Me*

LEARN

■ The pronoun *I* is a subject pronoun. It is used in the subject of a sentence. *I* is always capitalized.

I went to Tina's garage sale in May.

■ The pronoun *me* is an object pronoun. It is used after an action verb or a word such as *to, for, at,* and *from.*

Tina sold **me** a blue bicycle.
The bicycle was the right size **for me**.

■ When you speak or write about another person and yourself, it is polite to name yourself last. Follow the rules above for when to use *I* and *me.*

In June, **my sister and I** held a garage sale.
My mother helped **my sister and me**.

PRACTICE

A *Write the pronoun in ( ) that correctly completes each sentence.*

1. At the garage sale, _____ sold my old dolls. (I, me)

2. My sister and _____ also sold some books and clothes. (I, me)

3. Tina visited my sister and _____ at the garage sale. (I, me)

4. Tina asked _____ about the blue bicycle in my garage. (I, me)

5. She had sold the bike to _____ last month. (I, me)

6. Will you sell my old bike back to _____? (I, me)

7. My sister and _____ both wanted to keep the bike. (I, me)

8. Tina gave _____ such a sad look. (I, me)

9. _____ agreed to sell the bike back to Tina. (I, me)

10. Tina thanked _____ and rode off. (I, me)

B *Write the word or words in ( ) that correctly complete each sentence.*

1. My brother Nate gave _____ a baseball
two years ago. (I, me)

2. _____ sold it to Mrs. Green at our
garage sale. (Mom and I, I and Mom)

3. Nate got angry at _____. (I, me)

4. _____ felt terrible. (Mom and I, Mom and me)

5. _____ went over to Mrs. Green's house
the next day. (I, me)

6. Mrs. Green looked at _____ sadly and
explained what happened. (I, me)

7. _____ lost that ball playing with our dog.
(Me and my husband, My husband and I)

8. _____ have a baseball signed by a
famous player. (Mr. Green and I, Mr. Green and me)

9. Mrs. Green gave _____
the signed baseball, and I put it on our
table. (I, me)

10. Nate gave _____
a big smile. (Mom and me, me and Mom)

C *This story has six mistakes in the use of **I** and **me**. Find the mistakes, and use the proofreading marks in the box to correct them.*

My brother John and me wanted to sell things at the neighborhood yard sale. My mother let I look for things in the basement. Mom put prices on all the objects. Then I and John carried them up to the front yard. The stuff looked like junk to him and me.

There was one old dish with a dove on it. Mom told John and I to sell it for five dollars. Someone asked us if we would sell it for two dollars. John and I were about to say yes.

Just then our neighbor Mr. Gray looked at the dish. "My wife and me collect old dishes," he said. "This one is very old and valuable. Don't sell it!"

Mr. Gray was right. The dish turned out to be worth $500. Mom, John, and me were all amazed. That was the best yard sale ever!

Proofreading Marks

∧	Add
⊙	Period
ℰ	Take out
≡	Capital letter
/	Small letter

Look Back Did you correct six mistakes in the use of *I* and *me*?

WRITE

D *Each pair of sentences below is the same except for a noun and a pronoun. Use the word **and** to combine the noun and pronoun to form one sentence. The first one is done for you.*

1. I sold action figures at the neighborhood sale.
Tommy sold action figures at the neighborhood sale.

Tommy and I sold action figures at the neighborhood sale.

2. Terry sold me some comic books.
Terry sold Maria some comic books.

_____

3. Jenna bought some old board games.
I bought some old board games.

_____

4. Mr. Lee gave me some baseball cards.
Mr. Lee gave Juan some baseball cards.

_____

5. I found some T-shirts at the sale.
Kay found some T-shirts at the sale.

_____

6. Sam sold me some puzzles.
Sam sold Barbara some puzzles.

_____

7. I found wonderful things at the sale.
My friend found wonderful things at the sale.

_____

Lesson 38: **Possessive Pronouns**

LEARN

- A possessive noun shows *who* or *what* owns or has something. A **possessive pronoun** takes the place of a possessive noun.

   Maria's heroes are firefighters. **Her** heroes are firefighters.
   Actors are **the boys'** heroes. Actors are **their** heroes.

- The possessive pronouns below are used before nouns.
   my   your   his   her   its   our   their

   Do you and **your** classmates know any heroes?
   My brother is famous for **his** home run record in Little League.

Do not use an apostrophe with possessive pronouns.

PRACTICE

A *Write the possessive pronoun in each sentence.*

1. People have always told stories about their heroes. _____

2. Our country has many heroes. _____

3. These heroes are part of its history. _____

4. One of my heroes is Rosa Parks. _____

5. Ms. Parks refused to give up her seat on a bus. _____

6. This act helped people fight for their rights. _____

7. Is Neil Armstrong one of your heroes? _____

8. He is famous for his walk on the Moon. _____

9. The whole astronaut team can be proud of its work. _____

10. We look up to heroes for their great deeds. _____

B *Rewrite the second sentence in each pair. Replace the word or words in **dark print** with a possessive pronoun. The first one is done for you.*

1. Jill loves tall tales. **The tales'** make-believe heroes have fantastic adventures.

Their make-believe heroes have fantastic adventures.

2. Paul Bunyan was a lumberjack. **Paul Bunyan's** job was cutting down trees.

_____

3. Real-life lumberjacks made up stories about Paul Bunyan. **The lumberjacks'** tales say Paul was 50 feet tall!

_____

4. Mrs. Bunyan was big, too. **Mrs. Bunyan's** house was the size of Minnesota.

_____

5. Paul had a blue ox as big as a mountain. **The blue ox's** name was Babe.

_____

6. In one story, Paul dragged his ax along the ground. **The ax's** sharp edge made the Grand Canyon!

_____

C *Write a possessive pronoun to complete each sentence. Choose a possessive pronoun from the box. You will use some pronouns more than once.*

| my | your | his | her | its | our | their |

Baseball is one of _____ country's favorite
(1)

sports. Do you and _____ friends have any
(2)

baseball heroes? I do. One of _____ heroes is
(3)

Roberto Clemente. _____ baseball skills got him
(4)

elected to the Baseball Hall of Fame. A youth club in

Florida was named after Clemente. _____
(5)

purpose was to help Hispanic youth.

Babe Ruth is another one of _____ heroes in
(6)

the Baseball Hall of Fame. He set a record for home runs,

and _____ record was the best for 34 years.
(7)

Did you know that women played in a baseball

league, too? _____ league played for 12 years.
(8)

Dottie Schroeder was the only woman who played

all 12 seasons for the league. _____ picture
(9)

is in the exhibit on Women in Baseball in the

Baseball Hall of Fame.

Roberto Clemente

Write Your Own

WRITE

D Read each sentence. Then write a sentence that tells what happens next. Use a possessive pronoun in the sentence you write. The first one is done for you.

1. A fire-breathing dragon was outside the castle. _____

Its breath was melting the castle walls.

2. The people in the castle were afraid. _____

_____

3. The king called the people together. _____

_____

4. The prince could not fight the dragon. _____

_____

5. The people could not decide what to do. _____

_____

6. The princess rode out to fight the dragon _____

_____

7. The dragon was surprised to see a princess. _____

_____

8. In the end, the people had a new hero. _____

_____

Proofreading Checklist ✓

❏ *Did you use a possessive pronoun in each sentence?*

Lesson 39: **Pronoun-Antecedent Agreement**

LEARN

A **pronoun** is a word that takes the place of a noun. The noun the pronoun refers to is called the pronoun's **antecedent**. In each of the four examples below, the noun in **dark print** is the antecedent of the pronoun in **dark print**.

Thomas Edison at his laboratory

> **Thomas Edison** was an inventor.
> **He** invented many things we use today.

> He took **machines** apart to see how **they** worked.

> The young **man** fixed some broken equipment. As a result, the company gave **him** a job.

> The **inventor** spent many hours working in **his** laboratory.

■ A pronoun must agree with its antecedent in number. This means that if the noun is singular, the pronoun must also be singular. If the noun is plural, the pronoun must also be plural.

In the first example above, the singular pronoun *He* refers to the singular noun *Thomas Edison*. In the second example, the plural pronoun *they* refers to the plural noun *machines*. In the third and fourth examples, what do the singular pronouns *him* and *his* refer to?

PRACTICE

A *Look at the underlined pronoun. Write the noun that is its antecedent. The first one is done for you.*

1. Edison went to school for a short time. He did poorly there.

   Edison

2. His mother was a teacher. She taught Edison at home. _____

3. When Edison was twelve years old, he started his first job. _____

4. Edison worked on passenger trains. <u>They</u> were just becoming popular in the United States.

_____

5. Edison used a special alphabet when he was fifteen years old. <u>It</u> was called the Morse code.

_____

6. Edison started to lose <u>his</u> hearing at a young age.

_____

7. Edison had various jobs, but he was not interested in <u>them</u>.

_____

8. Edison decided to become an inventor. <u>His</u> first invention was a failure.

_____

B *Write the pronoun in ( ) that correctly completes each sentence. Think about whether the antecedent is singular or plural.*

1. After he became an inventor, Edison and his

wife married. _____ had three children. (He, They)

2. They moved to a new home. _____ was a quiet place for Edison to work. (They, It)

3. The phonograph was one of Edison's inventions. _____ played back his words. (It, They)

4. Inventors from all over the world worked for Edison. They helped

him with _____ many creations. (his, their)

5. Edison and his team used _____ many skills. (his, their)

6. Edison started the first research lab. He called _____ the "Invention Factory." (him, it)

7. Today, we still use many of Edison's inventions. _____ are important in our lives even now. (They, He)

C *Elise wrote this description about one of Edison's inventions. She made six mistakes when using pronouns. Find the mistakes, and use the proofreading marks to correct them.*

Thomas Edison did not invent the first lightbulb. In fact, scientists had been making lightbulbs before they did. Edison's achievement was making a lightbulb that people could use in his homes. Until Edison's invention, lightbulbs burned out after a few minutes. With the help of their team, Edison experimented with making the lightbulb better. Finally, in 1879, Edison and his team discovered something that worked. A small wire was placed in a lightbulb. They glowed for 13½ hours.

After Edison improved the lightbulb, it helped improve New York City's electric power system. He built a power station that brought electricity to the city so that lightbulbs could be used in people's homes. The power station opened in Manhattan. Customers within a mile of them were able to get electricity.

Proofreading Marks

∧	Add
⊙	Period
ℓ	Take out
≡	Capital letter
/	Small letter

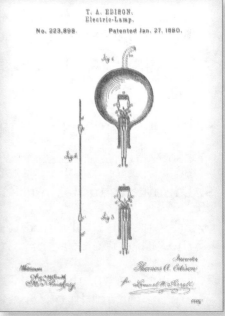

T. A. EDISON,
Electric-Lamp.
No. 223,898.   Patented Jan. 27, 1880.

Did you find and correct six pronouns?

WRITE

D Write a short description of an invention you enjoy. You could write about a new electronic device, for example. Include at least five pronouns in your sentences. Make sure that the pronouns agree with their antecedents.

_____

_____

_____

_____

_____

_____

_____

_____

_____

_____

_____

_____

You used formal language when you wrote your description. However, if you were talking to a friend about the invention, you might use sentence fragments and informal words such as wow *and* cool.

Proofreading Checklist ☑

❑ *Does each pronoun agree with its antecedent?*

Lesson 40: **Contractions with Pronouns**

LEARN

A **contraction** is two words written as one.
An apostrophe (') takes the place of one or more
letters that are left out. Many contractions are formed
by joining a pronoun and a verb.

> She sells seashells when **she is** at the seashore.
> She sells seashells when **she's** at the seashore.

> **She will** sell many seashore shells.
> **She'll** sell many seashore shells.

Contractions with					
am, is, are		**will**		**have, has**	
I am	**I'm**	I will	**I'll**	I have	**I've**
you are	**you're**	you will	**you'll**	you have	**you've**
he is	**he's**	he will	**he'll**	he has	**he's**
she is	**she's**	she will	**she'll**	she has	**she's**
it is	**it's**	it will	**it'll**	it has	**it's**
we are	**we're**	we will	**we'll**	we have	**we've**
they are	**they're**	they will	**they'll**	they have	**they've**

PRACTICE

A *Write the contraction for each pair of words.*

1. I am _____

2. you are _____

3. I have _____

4. they will _____

5. it will _____

6. they have _____

7. it has _____

8. you will _____

9. they are _____

10. he is _____

B *Rewrite each tongue twister. Replace the words in **dark print** with a contraction.*

1. Shy Shelly says **she will** sew sheets soon. _____

_____

2. **We are** watching window washers while we walk. _____

_____

3. Tonight **you have** no need to light a night light. _____

_____

4. **I have** never felt a foot of felt as fine as that. _____

_____

5. **She has** seen six seals. _____

_____

6. Friendly Frank says **he will** flip fine flapjacks. _____

_____

7. Surely **we will** see the sun shine soon. _____

_____

8. No, **we have** no two-toed tree toads. _____

_____

9. **They have** thirty-three thick things to throw. _____

_____

10. **He has** edited it with Ed. _____

_____

C *A group of students made up this list of tongue twisters. The students made six mistakes when writing contractions. Find the mistakes, and use the proofreading marks in the box to correct them.*

Tongue Twisters

- Betty bought better butter, but its bitter better butter.

- We'll willingly watch Willy's wristwatch.

- Theyll tie the note in a tight new knot.

- The little beetles are being bitten by the big bugs, but theyre biting the big bugs right back.

- Ive a saw that outsaws any saw Iv'e ever seen.

- He's baked some good baked goods.

- You'are really ready already!

- These tongue twisters are tricky, and they've twisted on my tongue.

Look Back **Did you correct six contractions?**

WRITE

D *Write your own sentences about seashells at the seashore.
In each sentence, use a contraction for the words in ( ).*

1. (they will) _____

_____

2. (he is) _____

_____

3. (you are) _____

_____

4. (we have) _____

_____

5. (I am) _____

_____

6. (it will) _____

_____

7. (she has) _____

_____

8. (we are) _____

_____

*Read the sentences you wrote. Notice how casual and informal the
contractions make the sentences sound. If you were writing a report,
however, you should not use too many contractions.*

Proofreading Checklist ✓

❏ *Did you use a contraction in each sentence?*
❏ *Did you spell each contraction correctly?*

Subject Pronouns (pp. 156–159) *Write the subject pronoun in each sentence.*

1. I look for stars on a clear night.   _____

2. They twinkle brightly in the night sky.   _____

3. We use a telescope to look at the stars.   _____

4. It is a gift from Uncle Larry.   _____

Pronoun-Verb Agreement (pp. 160–163) *Write the verb in ( ) that correctly completes each sentence.*

5. We (watch, watches) the stars with a telescope.   _____

6. I (help, helps) my mother set it up.   _____

7. She (point, points) out different stars.   _____

8. They (flash, flashes) in the dark, clear sky.   _____

Object Pronouns (pp. 164–167) *Write the object pronoun in each sentence.*

9. Mom shows me certain groups of stars.   _____

10. We call them constellations.   _____

11. The Big Dipper has seven stars in it.   _____

12. They all twinkle at us tonight.   _____

Using _I_ and _Me_ (pp. 168–171) _Underline the word or words in ( ) that correctly complete each sentence._

13. The stars fascinate Mom and (I, me).

14. My brother and (I, me) want to learn more about the stars.

15. (My family and I, Me and my family) will visit a planetarium.

16. The exhibits will amaze (my brother and me, my brother and I).

Possessive Pronouns (pp. 172–175) _Write the possessive pronoun in each sentence._

17. I see a star from my window. _____

18. Its light brightens the night sky. _____

19. The stars seem to change as our Earth spins. _____

20. They don't really change their positions. _____

Pronoun-Antecedent Agreement (pp. 176–179) _Look at the underlined pronoun. Write the noun that is its antecedent._

21. Aunt Helen is an astronomer. <u>She</u> works in a lab. _____

22. Astronomers study the stars and planets. In fact, <u>they</u> study all natural objects in space. _____

23. Aunt Helen has a telescope. She uses <u>it</u> in her work. _____

24. Here's a good tip for using the telescope. I must try <u>it</u>. _____

Contractions with Pronouns (pp. 180–183) _Read each sentence. Write the contraction for each pair of words in_ **dark print**.

25. **You are** sure to see stars tonight. _____

26. **She has** picked the best spot to view the stars. _____

27. **They have** seen a shooting star already. _____

28. **We will** watch for shooting stars, too. _____

Unit 5 Test

DIRECTIONS *Fill in the circle next to the sentence that shows the correct spelling and use of pronouns, verbs, and contractions.*

1. ○ Me and my classmates study dinosaurs in Mr. Kelly's class.

   ○ He take us to the museum to learn more.

   ○ Miguel and me sit together.

   ○ They wait anxiously.

2. ○ We all rushes to the Hall of Dinosaurs.

   ○ I wants to see the T. rex.

   ○ You'are to walk slowly!

   ○ It's a rule in this museum!

3. ○ Tell Bob and me about the word *dinosaur*.

   ○ It mean "terrible lizard."

   ○ The fossils don't look terrible to Miguel and I.

   ○ A guard leaves its station to tell us why dinosaurs died.

4. ○ Miguel and me like the dinosaurs the most.

   ○ They're putting up many new displays in the museum.

   ○ We reads about one display.

   ○ "The Age of Reptiles" is her name.

5. ○ Mr. Kelly shows me and my classmates the apatosaurus.

   ○ It measures over 75 feet long.

   ○ I watches its tiny head.

   ○ It seem to move.

6. ○ The huge T. rex gets our's attention next.

   ○ It's size was her scariest feature.

   ○ It gives some of us the shivers.

   ○ Me am glad none are around today.

7. ○ Me and the others study the diplodocus.

   ○ It weigh more than ten elephants.

   ○ It are bigger than the apatosaurus.

   ○ Its neck is very long.

8. ○ The museum displays their small dinosaurs, too.

   ○ We see one dinosaur that is the size of a chicken.

   ○ Us also saw a fossil of a dinosaur with feathers.

   ○ Well never see anything like that in a zoo.

DIRECTIONS *Read the paragraphs, and look at each underlined part. Fill in the circle next to the answer choice that shows the correct spelling and use of pronouns, verbs, and contractions. If the underlined part is already correct, fill in the circle for "Correct as is."*

My family and me camp in Montana. Last summer, my brother Jed
 (9)   (10)
and me found something there that was incredible.
 (10)

We were sitting on rocks around a campfire. "Me think your seat is a
                                              (11)
fossil," Jed said to Dad and me. Dad looked at it carefully. "Yes, it's a
              (12)   (13)
fossil. They're always finding fossils around here," he said.
        (13)

Dad called the Dinosaur Field Station the next morning. A scientist

came to look at the fossil. He thanked Dad, Jed, and I for finding it.
                                       (14)

9. ○ Me and my family camp
○ My family and I camp
○ I and my family camp
○ Correct as is

12. ○ Jed said to Dad and I
○ Jed said to I and Dad
○ Jed said to me and Dad
○ Correct as is

10. ○ I and my brother Jed
○ me and my brother Jed
○ my brother Jed and I
○ Correct as is

13. ○ Yes, its a fossil. They're always
○ Yes, it's a fossil. They'ar always
○ Yes, its a fossil. They'ar always
○ Correct as is

11. ○ Me thinks
○ I think
○ I thinks
○ Correct as is

14. ○ I, Dad, and Jed
○ me, Dad, and Jed
○ Dad, Jed, and me
○ Correct as is

Lesson 41: Writing Sentences Correctly

LEARN

Use capital letters and end marks to write sentences correctly. Begin every sentence with a capital letter. End every sentence with an end mark.

- **End a statement with a period (.).**
  The blue whale is the largest animal.

- **End a question with a question mark (?).**
  Does it really weigh 200 tons?

- **End a command with a period (.).**
  Look at its tail.

- **End an exclamation with an exclamation mark (!).**
  Blue whales are huge!

Blue whale

PRACTICE

A Write the correct end mark to end each sentence. Then write **statement, question, command,** or **exclamation** to tell what kind of sentence it is.

1. Listen to this ____   _____

2. A blue whale can weigh more than 20 elephants ____   _____

3. How much does it eat in one day ____   _____

4. A blue whale can eat 4 tons of food a day ____   _____

5. What an appetite it must have ____   _____

6. A baby blue whale can be 25 feet long ____   _____

7. That is a really big baby ____   _____

8. Watch the whale dive ____   _____

9. Will it stay underwater long ____   _____

10. Some blue whales stay underwater a whole hour ____   _____

B *Rewrite each sentence. Use capital letters and end marks correctly.*

1. the giant squid lives more than half a mile under the sea _____

_____

2. tell me more about this sea creature _____

_____

3. it can grow to be almost 60 feet long _____

_____

4. that's really amazing _____

_____

5. could a giant squid sink a ship _____

_____

6. that isn't very likely _____

_____

7. giant squid sometimes attack whales _____

_____

8. what a terrible underwater battle that must be _____

_____

C Read this description of sharks. Three sentences in the description are missing capital letters. Four sentences are missing end marks. Find the mistakes, and use the proofreading marks in the box to correct them.

Sharks

Sharks can hear other fish more than half a mile away Their powerful bodies slice through the sea. their teeth are very sharp. How frightening sharks often seem

Do you think all sharks attack humans Think again. Over 400 types of sharks live in the ocean. only a few types are dangerous.

Listen to more good news Sharks attack fewer than 100 people each year. only a few of these attacks are deadly. In fact, more people die from bee stings than from shark attacks.

Proofreading Marks

∧	Add
⊙	Period
ℰ	Take out
≡	Capital letter
/	Small letter

Did you find seven mistakes in the sentences?

WRITE

D *Rewrite this bulletin-board notice to make it more inviting. Change each sentence in **dark print** to another kind of sentence. The word in ( ) tells you the kind of sentence to write. You may have to change the wording in some of the sentences.*

Science Club Trip to Aquarium

Bayville has a splashy new aquarium. (exclamation) The Science Club is planning a trip there on Saturday, May 3. Would you like to see dolphins and orcas? Would you like to see sharks and squid? **Anyone can sign up for the trip today.** (command)

Do you have questions about the aquarium trip? **Then you can talk to Ms. Sarno.** (command) **This is going to be a fun-filled trip.** (exclamation)

Lesson 42: **Capitalizing Proper Nouns**

LEARN

A **proper noun** names a specific person, place, or thing. A proper noun may be one or more words. Each important word begins with a capital letter.

- Begin the name of a person or pet with a capital letter.

    Angela   James Jones   Rover

- Begin the name of a specific place with a capital letter.

    Main Street (street)
    North Dakota (state)
    Catskill Mountains (mountains)
    Gulf of Mexico (body of water)
    New York City (city)
    United States (country)

- Begin the name of a holiday, a day of the week, or a month with a capital letter.

    Thanksgiving   Thursday   November

PRACTICE

A *Write each proper noun correctly.*

1. june _____

2. lake erie _____

3. saturday _____

4. california _____

5. eddie _____

6. juan ramos _____

7. salt lake city _____

8. fourth of july _____

9. newton avenue _____

10. puerto rico _____

B *Rewrite each sentence. Capitalize each proper noun correctly.*

1. We picked blueberries along blueberry lane. _____

_____

2. On bear mountain, we saw a bear. _____

_____

3. Tom swam in the river near river city, iowa. _____

_____

4. Gina grows roses on rose avenue. _____

_____

5. Is lake placid a beautiful lake? _____

_____

6. The rocky mountains are great for mountain climbing. _____

_____

7. We had a fun day on monday. _____

_____

8. Is rhode island an island? _____

_____

9. I may visit you and maria in may. _____

_____

10. What's new in new jersey? _____

_____

C Dori wrote an invitation for her birthday party. She wrote two nouns with capital letters when she shouldn't have. She forgot to write six nouns with capital letters when she should have. Find the mistakes, and use the proofreading marks in the box to correct them.

Remember 💡
Each important word in a proper noun begins with a capital letter.

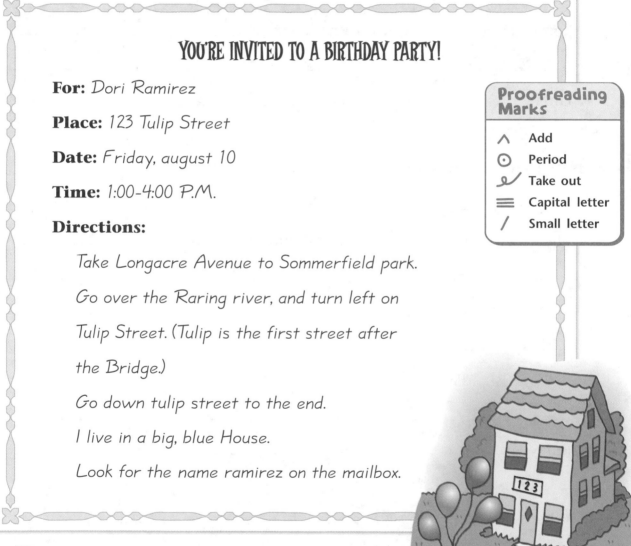

YOU'RE INVITED TO A BIRTHDAY PARTY!

For: Dori Ramirez

Place: 123 Tulip Street

Date: Friday, august 10

Time: 1:00-4:00 P.M.

Directions:

Take Longacre Avenue to Sommerfield park.

Go over the Raring river, and turn left on

Tulip Street. (Tulip is the first street after

the Bridge.)

Go down tulip street to the end.

I live in a big, blue House.

Look for the name ramirez on the mailbox.

Proofreading Marks

∧	Add
⊙	Period
ℓ	Take out
≡	Capital letter
/	Small letter

Did you correct eight nouns?

WRITE

D *Imagine you are having a party. What kind of party would it be? Where and when would you have it? Complete the invitation below. Write directions for how to get to the party.*

Additional Resources at
grammarworkshop.com

YOU'RE INVITED TO A _____

For: _____

Place: _____

Date: _____

Time: _____

Directions:

_____

_____

_____

_____

_____

_____

_____

Proofreading Checklist ✓

❏ *Did you begin each proper noun with a capital letter?*

❏ *Did you begin each important word in the proper noun with a capital letter?*

Lesson 43: **Abbreviations**

LEARN

An **abbreviation** is a short form of a word.
Many abbreviations begin with a capital letter
and end with a period.

- **You can abbreviate the days of the week.**

  Mon.   Tues.   Wed.   Thurs.
  Fri.   Sat.   Sun.

- **You can abbreviate some months of the year.
  The months May, June, and July do not
  have abbreviations.**

  Jan.   Feb.   Mar.   Apr.   Aug.
  Sept.   Oct.   Nov.   Dec.

- **A title of respect is often used with a person's name.
  Most titles of respect are written as abbreviations.**

  Ms. Janine Navarro   **Mr.** William Tran
  Mrs. Helen Winters   **Dr.** Dennis Martin

- **An initial is an abbreviation for a person's first or middle name.
  It is written as a capital letter followed by a period.**

  Anita **R.** Velez   **J. D.** Simmons

PRACTICE

A *Write the abbreviation for each day, month, and name correctly.*

1. Feb _____

2. oct. _____

3. Wed _____

4. jan. _____

5. thurs _____

6. dr. Anne e. Ross _____

7. mr. Eric Cohen _____

8. ms Lee _____

9. Mrs Irene Walters _____

10. Martin N Rios _____

B *Rewrite each day, month, or name below according to the directions in ( ). Use capital letters and periods correctly.*

1. Saturday _____
(Change to the abbreviation.)

2. September _____
(Change to the abbreviation.)

3. Andrew Greenfield _____
(Change the first name to an initial.)

4. Laura Ann Bridges _____
(Change the middle name to an initial.)

5. Sandra Flores _____
(Add the title of respect for a doctor.)

6. Alison Weaver _____
(Add the title of respect for a woman.)

7. Stanley Robert Teng _____
(Change the first and middle names to initials.)

8. Tuesday _____
(Change to the abbreviation.)

9. David Singer _____
(Add the title of respect for a doctor.)

10. Linda Robinson _____
(Add the title of respect for a woman.)

11. December _____
(Change to the abbreviation.)

12. John Moore _____
(Add the title of respect for a man.)

C *Here is a schedule for a school event that will take place throughout the year. Five abbreviations are missing capital letters, and five are missing periods. Look for the mistakes, and correct them. Use the proofreading marks in the box.*

Proofreading Marks

∧	Add
⊙	Period
ℒ	Take out
≡	Capital letter
/	Small letter

Sandy Hill School
Favorite Authors Festival

Date	Event
Wed., Oct 16	Author Wanda E. Brown will read from her new biography of J. k. Rowling.
Mon., nov. 9	Ms Ward will read chapters from several books by Laura Ingalls Wilder.
Tues., Dec. 14	Mr. Miley's students will show their drawings of books by E B. White.
Fri., Jan. 22	The Theater Club will put on a play based on the Winnie-the-Pooh books by A. A Milne.
mon., Feb. 25	ms. Chen will present a display of science books by Millicent E. Selsam.
Thurs., Mar. 8	Ms. Pierce and Mrs Wilkins will read aloud books by dr. Seuss to kindergarten classes.

LOOK Back **Did you correct ten mistakes with abbreviations?**

Write Your Own

WRITE

D Write a schedule for a school author festival that includes your favorite authors. Use the schedule on page 198 as a model. Write the day and month of each event as abbreviations. Write a teacher's name and an author's name for each event. Include a title of respect or an initial in each name.

Favorite Authors Festival

Date	Event

Proofreading Checklist ✓

❏ Did you begin each abbreviation with a capital letter and end it with a period?

❏ Did you write each initial with a capital letter followed by a period?

Lesson 44: **Book Titles**

LEARN

- When typed, titles of books often appear in italics. When you write by hand, underline book titles.

  TYPED   I read *Look at the Pictures*.

  WRITTEN BY HAND   I read <u>Look at the Pictures</u>.

- Capitalize the first word and each important word in a book title. Do not capitalize the words *a, an, and, at, for, in, of, on, the,* or *to* unless they are the first word in the title.

  The Wind in the Willows
  Young Cam Jansen and the Library Mystery

PRACTICE

A *Rewrite each book title. Capitalize and underline each title correctly.*

1. a Nest Full Of eggs   _____

2. Goldilocks And The Three Bears   _____

3. The cat in The Hat   _____

4. when lightning comes in a jar   _____

5. the Wright brothers   _____

6. My side Of the Mountain   _____

7. The Princess And The Pizza   _____

8. my Visit To the aquarium   _____

9. Fox On stage   _____

10. in The Time of the drums   _____

B *Rewrite each sentence. Capitalize and underline each title correctly.*

1. Horrible harry goes to Sea tells of a class trip on a riverboat.

_____

2. Ben Franklin And His first Kite tells about Ben at the age of ten.

_____

3. A boy and his horse help people in Rescue On The outer banks.

_____

4. Nine animals and the Well is a story about friendship.

_____

5. For a good laugh, read Gila monsters meet you at the airport.

_____

6. The sword in the tree takes place in a knight's castle.

_____

7. Arrow To The Sun retells a Pueblo Indian story.

_____

8. A good collection of mind-bending puzzles is Math For all Seasons.

_____

9. A girl gets an unusual birthday present in I Have An olive tree.

_____

10. One of my favorite books is Charlie and the Chocolate factory.

_____

C Rob made nine mistakes when writing the book titles in his book descriptions. He capitalized five words by mistake, and he forgot to capitalize two words. He also forgot to underline two titles. Find the mistakes, and use the proofreading marks to correct them.

Remember
Capitalize the first word and each important word in a book title. Underline the title.

Rob's Favorite Books

Learning geography can be fun! If you don't believe me, read <u>The Scrambled states Of America</u>. This book is packed with weird facts and funny pictures.

The crew members of a spaceship are looking for an adventure. That's just what they find in Commander Toad and The Planet of The Grapes.

Poor Edward wants only two things. He wants to have a dog and to be free of the bully Martin. Does he succeed? Read <u>a Dog On Barkham Street</u> by Mary Stolz to find out.

Everyone knows foxes are clever, and naturally they make great detectives! Find out how great in Flatfoot Fox And the Case of the Nosy Otter.

Proofreading Marks

∧	Add
⊙	Period
ℓ	Take out
≡	Capital letter
/	Small letter

Did you correct nine mistakes in the book titles?

Write Your Own

WRITE

D *Read the description of each book. Then make up a title for the book. Write the title correctly on the line.*

1. Stripe the zebra wants to be the best batter on the zoo baseball team.

_____

2. Barry is riding his bike in the park, and he meets a dragon.

_____

3. This nonfiction book looks at some common insects.

_____

4. In 1845, eight-year-old Jason crosses the country in a covered wagon.

_____

5. On a hot summer day, two friends find an unusual way to cool off.

_____

6. This nonfiction book explores the mysterious world under the sea.

_____

7. Should the smartest student in Room 3B be elected class president?

_____

8. This book tells how Thomas Jefferson wrote the Declaration of Independence.

_____

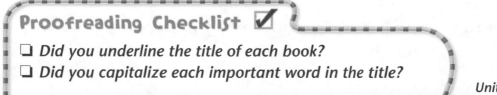

Proofreading Checklist ☑

❏ *Did you underline the title of each book?*
❏ *Did you capitalize each important word in the title?*

Lesson 45: Commas in a Series

LEARN

A **comma** separates words or ideas in a sentence and tells the reader when to pause. A comma helps to make the meaning of a sentence clear.

A list of three or more words in a sentence is called a **series**. Use a comma to separate the words in a series.

> **Students, teachers, and parents** all work together in our school.
> Students get to school by **bus, car, and bike**.

PRACTICE

A *The words in **dark print** are a series. Add commas to separate the words.*

1. My friends **Joan Mary and Rita** are in my class.

2. **Reading math and art** are our subjects this morning.

3. Our book has many **poems stories and plays**.

4. **Greg Tonya and Juan** take turns reading aloud.

5. Then we work on **addition subtraction and multiplication**.

6. We read about our **city state and country** in social studies.

7. We play **tag dodgeball and hide-and-seek** on the playground.

8. The **slides swings and seesaws** are always busy.

9. One lunch choice today is pizza with **cheese mushrooms and peppers**.

10. Another choice is a sandwich with **turkey lettuce and tomato**.

B *Write the series in each sentence. Add commas to separate the words in the series.*

1. We write letters poems and stories during language arts.

   _____

2. We also find nouns verbs and adjectives in sentences.

   _____

3. I like science more than math reading and social studies.

   _____

4. The sun stars and planets are my favorite topics.

   _____

5. Oceans deserts and rainforests are also interesting.

   _____

6. Mondays Wednesdays and Fridays are gym days.

   _____

7. I use crayons clay and paint in art class.

   _____

8. Paint sometimes drips on the tables chairs and floor.

   _____

9. Flutes drums and other instruments fill the music room.

   _____

10. Songs dances and laughter also fill it!

   _____

C Write a series of three words from the box to complete each sentence. Use commas where they are needed.

batting	bat	April	first base	double
fielding	glove	May	shortstop	triple
running	helmet	June	center field	home run

1. I play on the school baseball team during _____

_____ and _____ .

2. We work on _____ _____ and

_____ at baseball practice.

3. I got a new baseball _____ _____ and

_____ for my birthday.

4. I like to pitch, but I can also play _____ _____

and _____ .

5. I hit a _____ _____ and

_____ in one big game.

Combining Sentences

WRITE

Sometimes you can combine short and choppy sentences into one longer and smoother sentence.

Each sentence below has a subject that tells who helps out at home.

> **My brothers** help out at home.
> **My sisters** help out at home.
> **I** help out at home.

Putting these subjects in a series makes one smooth sentence.

> **My brothers, my sisters, and I** help out at home.

 Additional Resources at grammarworkshop.com

D *Rewrite each group of sentences. Combine them into one sentence.*

1. I wash the dishes. I wash the windows. I wash the kitchen floor. _____

_____

2. My brothers sweep the sidewalk. My brothers sweep the garage.

My brothers sweep the basement. _____

_____

3. My sisters get buckets. My sisters get mops. My sisters get dust cloths.

_____

4. I rake up leaves. I rake up grass clippings. I rake up branches. _____

_____

5. Flowers grow in the yard. Trees grow in the yard. Bushes grow in the yard.

_____

Lesson 46: **Parts of a Letter**

LEARN

Use capital letters and commas correctly in each
part of a friendly letter.

> 9988 Central Avenue
> Boston, MA 02108 ← **heading**
> June 1, 2013
>
> Dear Aunt Mae, ← **greeting**
>   Last Thanksgiving, you suggested that I visit
> you and Uncle Tyrell at your farm some time. ← **body**
> May I come this summer? I'd love to spend some
> time in the country.
>
>   Your niece, ← **closing**
>   Barbara ← **signature**

HEADING
Use a comma between the city and state.
Use a comma between the day and the year in the date.

GREETING
Begin with a capital letter, and end with a comma.

CLOSING
Begin with a capital letter, and end with a comma.

PRACTICE

A *Write each part of the letter correctly.*

1. May 3 2013 _____

2. Akron OH 44326 _____

3. sincerely yours _____

4. dear kate _____

5. your friend _____

6. 510 maple lane _____

B *Complete each letter with the missing part.*
Write that part of the letter correctly.

harrisonburg, va 22807   88 mountain road   June 15 2013

_____

_____

_____

Dear Barbara,
　　We'd love to have you visit! Summer is a busy time at our farm. We have so much work to do. We might put you to work, too!
　　　　　　　　　　　　Sincerely yours,
　　　　　　　　　　　　Aunt Mae

love   dear aunt mae   Barbara

9988 Central Avenue
Boston, MA 02108
June 23, 2013

_____

　　I am a really hard worker. I love busy times, too! I'm probably just the person you need on the farm this summer.

_____

_____

C *Read these letters from Barbara. She didn't use capital letters in two places where she should have. She also left out four commas. Find the mistakes, and use the proofreading marks to correct them.*

Remember

Use commas between the city and state and the day and the year in the heading of a letter. Begin the greeting and the closing with a capital letter, and end with a comma.

88 Mountain Road
Harrisonburg, VA 22807
July 27 2013

dear Mom,

    Farm life is great! Every morning, I feed the piglets. Then I swim in the pond. There are 36 piglets. Do you think I can bring one home?

        Your daughter
        Barbara

Proofreading Marks

∧	Add
⊙	Period
ℒ	Take out
≡	Capital letter
/	Small letter

9988 Central Avenue
Boston MA 02108
August 12 2013

Dear Aunt Mae and Uncle Tyrell,

    Thank you for letting me visit you. I really liked your pigs. Everything was wonderful. I hope I see you next summer, too.

        love,
        Barbara

Did you correct the six mistakes?

WRITE

D On the lines below, write a letter to a friend or relative.
Invite that person to join you for a special event or to
thank him or her for something. Be creative.

_____

_____

_____

_____

_____

_____

_____

_____

_____

_____

_____

_____

Proofreading Checklist ☑

❏ *Did you write the heading correctly?*
❏ *Did you write the greeting correctly?*
❏ *Did you write the closing correctly?*

Lesson 47: Quotations

LEARN

When two people are having a conversation or dialogue, they are speaking to each other. **Quotation marks** show that a person is speaking. They show a speaker's exact words.

> John said, "Let's start a Helping Hands Club."

- **Put quotation marks before and after a speaker's words.**

  > Jean asked, "What would its purpose be?"

- **Use a comma to separate the other words in the sentence from the speaker's words.**

  > John explained, "We would help others in our community."

- **Capitalize the first word inside the quotation marks.**

  > Matt exclaimed, "That's a great idea!"

PRACTICE

A *Add quotation marks around each speaker's words.*

1. John said, We could help out at the Town Food Pantry.

2. Jean asked, Would they really want our help?

3. Lauren said, My grandmother volunteers there.

4. She added, They are always looking for helpers.

5. Matt said, Let's call them and volunteer.

6. Judy asked, What else could the Helping Hands Club do?

7. Ben said, The park ranger wants volunteers to clean up the park.

8. He added, We could do that on Saturday mornings.

9. John replied, I don't see why not.

10. Judy exclaimed, Ms. Kelly will love that idea!

B *Rewrite each sentence correctly. Add the missing comma and quotation marks. Capitalize the first word inside the quotation marks. The first one is done for you.*

1. Ray asked what is the Helping Hands Club doing these days? _____

 Ray asked, "What is the Helping Hands Club doing these days?"

2. Judy said we made get-well cards last week. _____

_____

3. She added we sent them to children in the hospital. _____

_____

4. John exclaimed the children and the nurses loved them! _____

_____

5. He continued now the nurses want us to read to the children. _____

_____

6. Judy explained my mother is taking us there on Saturday. _____

_____

7. She asked do you want to come with us, Ray? _____

_____

8. Ray replied that sounds interesting. _____

_____

C *Ben wrote down this conversation from a club meeting. When he wrote what the speakers said, he left out six quotation marks. He also forgot to use capital letters in two places. Find the mistakes, and use the proofreading marks in the box to correct them.*

Remember 💡
Use quotation marks to show the speaker's exact words. Use a comma to separate the speaker's words from other words. Capitalize the first word inside the quotation marks.

Matt asked, "Have you noticed the flower boxes outside our school recently?

Jean responded, "I didn't know we had flower boxes.

Matt explained, "That's because they never have flowers in them."

John declared, "The Helping Hands Club should do something about that!

Judy asked, "should we buy flowers for the window boxes?"

Matt replied, maybe some stores will give us flowers."

John agreed, "It's certainly worth asking."

Ray said, "I'll be glad to plant and water the flowers.

John joked, I wonder if helping hands have green thumbs."

Proofreading Marks

∧	Add
⊙	Period
ℒ	Take out
≡	Capital letter
/	Small letter

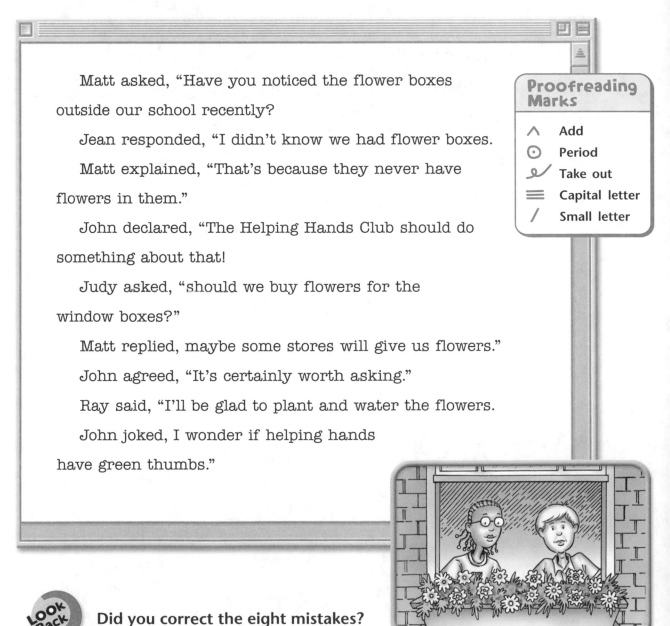

LOOK Back **Did you correct the eight mistakes?**

Write Your Own

WRITE

D *Rewrite each situation below to show each speaker's exact words. Put quotation marks around the exact words. Use Ben's writing on page 214 as a model.*

Situation 1 Jean wanted the club to pick up litter around the school. Ray disagreed with Jean. He thought the school had workers to clean up litter. Matt suggested that they ask the principal if the workers needed help.

_____

_____

_____

_____

Situation 2 Judy's little sister goes to a city day care center. The center has only a few storybooks for the children. John thinks the club can collect used books for the center. Ray thinks the club should collect at least 200 books.

_____

_____

_____

_____

You probably used contractions in the conversations you just wrote. When you speak, you often use contractions. When you complete a written assignment, however, do not use too many of them.

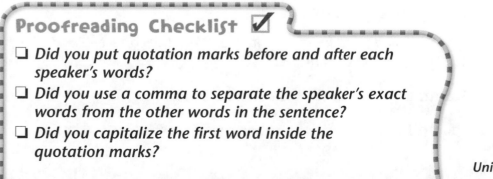

Proofreading Checklist ☑

❏ *Did you put quotation marks before and after each speaker's words?*

❏ *Did you use a comma to separate the speaker's exact words from the other words in the sentence?*

❏ *Did you capitalize the first word inside the quotation marks?*

Lesson 48: **Spelling Rules**

LEARN

■ It is helpful to remember the spellings of words that you use frequently in writing. Here are some frequently used words.

again	another	beautiful	different	favorite
friend	nothing	people	says	thought

■ A **suffix** is a word part that is added to the end of a word. Adding a suffix changes the meaning of the word. Use the rules below to correctly spell words with suffixes.

- **If the word ends in a consonant, simply add the suffix.**

  cook + ing = cooking   talk + ed = talked

- **If the word ends in a silent _e_, drop the _e_ before adding a suffix that begins with a vowel.**

  drive + ing = driving   smile + ed = smiled

- **If the word ends in a silent _e_, keep the _e_ and add the suffix that begins with a consonant.**

  grace + ful = graceful   move + ment = movement

- **For most words ending in a consonant and _y_, change the _y_ to an _i_ before adding any suffix, except suffixes that begin with _i_.**

  happy + ness = happiness   dry + est = driest
  deny + ing = denying

- **For one-syllable words that end in a single consonant, double the final consonant before adding the suffix.**

  stop + ing = stopping   thin + er = thinner

PRACTICE

A *Circle the misspelled word in each sentence. Write the correct spelling of the word on the line.*

1. We took annother trip to the amusement park yesterday.   _____

2. My frend and I did not ride the roller coaster last year.   _____

3. This year, I knew it would be diffrent. _____

4. We waited our turn on line along with the other peeple. _____

5. The beginning of the ride was my favrit part. _____

6. I could see the beutyful lights from high above. _____

7. When the roller coaster started to drop, I thot we would never stop falling! _____

8. Nuthing was as exciting as my first roller coaster ride. _____

9. I can't wait to go the amusement park ugain! _____

10. Sadly, my mom sez we will have to wait until next year. _____

B *Add a suffix to each word. Use the spelling rules to spell the word correctly. If you are not sure of the spelling, check a dictionary.*

1. care + ing   _____

2. pay + ment   _____

3. clap + ed   _____

4. kind+ ness   _____

5. grab + ed   _____

6. run + ing   _____

7. cry + ed   _____

8. easy + est   _____

9. scrape + ed   _____

10. help + ed   _____

11. color + ful   _____

12. bright + er   _____

On a separate sheet of paper, write a sentence using each of the words you wrote.

C Read this report about the first Ferris wheel. The writer made eight spelling mistakes. Find the mistakes, and use the proofreading marks to correct them.

Remember 💡
Use the spelling rules to help you correctly spell words with suffixes.

Proofreading Marks

∧	Add
⊙	Period
ℰ	Take out
≡	Capital letter
/	Small letter

The planners of the 1893 Chicago World's Fair thot long and hard. They wanted to construct something amazeing for the fair. They hopped that someone would have a great idea.

Then a bridge builder named George W. Ferris presented his idea for the Ferris wheel. After much discussion, the planners decided to build it. The completed structure had thirty-six wooden cars. Each car carryed up to sixty riders. It took twenty minutes to go around twice.

The planners of the Chicago World's Fair were hopful that the Ferris wheel would bring people to the fair. Well, it did! Peple loved the Ferris wheel. They would get off the ride and then get back on line to ride it agen.

Today, Ferris wheels are still popular. You can ride them at most fairs and amusement parks. They remain a favorit for young and old alike.

Did you correct eight spelling mistakes?

Write Your Own

WRITE

D *Imagine you are at an amusement park. Write sentences about your experience at the park. In your sentences, include some of the frequently used words in Learn on page 216 and some of the words with suffixes in Practice B on page 217.*

_____

_____

_____

_____

_____

_____

_____

_____

_____

_____

_____

_____

_____

_____

Proofreading Checklist ☑

❏ *Did you spell frequently used words correctly?*
❏ *Did you spell words with suffixes correctly?*

Lesson 49: **Words Often Misspelled**

LEARN

■ **Homophones** are words that sound the same but have different spellings and meanings.

pear	I ate a **pear** for dessert.
pair	I own a **pair** of brown boots.
hare	Do you see the **hare** eating grass?
hair	My sister has brown **hair**.
week	I spent a **week** preparing for my trip.
weak	The **weak** chair broke when I sat on it.

■ Some contractions and possessive pronouns are homophones.

you're	**You're** lucky to have found this book.
your	What is the title of **your** book?
it's	**It's** a book that has many adventures.
its	**Its** stories have entertained readers of all ages.
they're	**They're** sure to provide action and suspense.
their	**Their** heroes are very likeable characters.
there	**There** are very few books that are this exciting.

■ When you are not sure of the spelling of a word, check a dictionary.

PRACTICE

A *Match each word in Column A with its meaning in Column B. Write the letter of the meaning on the line. The first one is done for you.*

	A		B
_c_	**1.** you're		**a.** woodland animal
____	**2.** hare		**b.** in that place
____	**3.** there		**c.** you are
____	**4.** weak		**d.** a fruit
____	**5.** pear		**e.** not strong

____ **6.** your   **f.** two of something

____ **7.** week   **g.** seven days

____ **8.** pair   **h.** belonging to you

____ **9.** hair   **i.** they are

____ **10.** they're   **j.** tresses or curls

B *Write the word in ( ) that correctly completes each sentence.*

1. Is that _____ copy of *Little House on the Prairie*? (your, you're)

2. The book is next to the red _____ on the table. (pear, pair)

3. Laura Ingalls Wilder is _____ author. (its, it's)

4. If _____ looking for a great book, try the *Little House* stories. (your, you're)

5. These books are popular because _____ filled with humor and love. (there, they're)

6. In *The Long Winter*, the family members have to leave _____ home on the prairie. (their, they're)

7. It has snowed heavily all _____, and more snow is expected. (weak, week)

8. Several snowy months have passed, and

_____ is less and less food. (there, they're)

9. Everyone fears the young and the old will become

_____ if they do not have enough food to eat. (weak, week)

10. After months of snow, _____ time for the town to celebrate the end of winter. (its, it's)

Laura Ingalls Wilder,
author of *Little House* books

C *Diane wrote this description of the Ingalls Homestead. She spelled seven words incorrectly. Find the mistakes, and use the proofreading marks in the box to correct them.*

Remember

When spelling a homophone, think about the way it is used. Remember that the words *its, your,* and *their* are possessive pronouns. The words *it's, you're,* and *they're* are contractions.

Our family was interested in the Little House books, so we spent a weak visiting the Ingalls Homestead. It's located in De Smet, South Dakota. Five of Ms. Ingalls's stories are set their.

The Ingalls lived in several places in De Smet. You can see there farm as well as the house that Pa built in 1887. There is even a dugout house.

Its fun to visit De Smet. It's one-room schoolhouse is still standing. If you want, you can even take a class there. You can take a covered-wagon ride in De Smet, too. The prairie stretches far and wide. It feels like 1880 again.

The Homestead guides know all about the Ingalls family and its adventures. Their able to answer all you're questions. It's a great place to learn some history!

Proofreading Marks

∧	Add
⊙	Period
ℰ	Take out
≡	Capital letter
/	Small letter

 Did you correct seven spelling mistakes?

WRITE

D *Write to a friend about a place you have visited. Describe the people and things you saw there. Tell what makes the place special. Give some facts about the place, too. Use some of the words on page 220 when you write.*

_____

_____

_____

_____

_____

_____

_____

_____

_____

_____

_____

_____

_____

_____

_____

Read the sentences you wrote. Notice how casual and informal the contractions make the sentences sound. If you are writing a report, however, you should not use too many contractions.

Proofreading Checklist ✔

❏ *Did you use* its, your, *or* their *as possessive pronouns?*
❏ *Did you use* it's, you're, *or* they're *as contractions?*

Lesson 50: **Words Often Confused**

LEARN

- When two words sound alike or have almost the same spelling, the words can be confused. Learn the meaning and spelling of each word so that you know which one to use.

  Here is an example. Sometimes, the word *loose* is confused with the word *lose*. When something is *loose*, it is not attached firmly. When you *lose* something, you no longer have it.

  My tooth is **loose**. I will **lose** it soon!

  Think about how the easily confused words *missed* and *mist* are used in the sentences below.

  I **missed** the ball. I couldn't see it coming toward me in the morning **mist**.

- If you are unsure of which word to use, check a dictionary.

PRACTICE

A *Match each word in Column A with its meaning in Column B. Write the letter of the meaning on the line.*

A	B
____ **1.** passed	**a.** restfulness
____ **2.** quiet	**b.** a slice or section of
____ **3.** peace	**c.** very much or completely
____ **4.** breath	**d.** moved or went by
____ **5.** past	**e.** a gulp of air
____ **6.** piece	**f.** over and done with
____ **7.** quite	**g.** silent
____ **8.** breathe	**h.** inhale and exhale

B *Write the word in ( ) that correctly completes each sentence.*

1. Carla _____ her old friends when she moved to our school. (missed, mist)

2. She _____ the principal's office looking for the classroom. (passed, past)

3. Her new uniform was a little _____. (lose, loose)

4. Her hair was damp from the _____ outside. (mist, missed)

5. Everyone was _____ when she walked into the room. (quiet, quite)

6. She had to _____ deeply to calm down. (breath, breathe)

7. Maria walked with Carla in the hallways so that she wouldn't

   _____ her way. (lose, loose)

8. At lunch, Peter gave her a _____ of his snack. (peace, piece)

9. At the end of the day, Carla could barely catch her _____. (breath, breathe)

10. She felt _____ tired after all the excitement! (quiet, quite)

11. She welcomed the _____ and calm of her evening at home. (peace, piece)

12. It was already _____ her bedtime when she got in bed. (past, passed)

C *Choose a word from the box to complete each sentence.* Be sure to choose the word with the correct meaning.

breath	loose	missed	passed	quiet
breathe	lose	mist	past	quite

1. Poor Dan was having a bad day! He woke up late and _____ the bus.

2. There was a lot of _____ in the air, and his shirt became damp.

3. It was already half _____ eight when he turned the corner.

4. Dan bumped into Mrs. Jones as he _____ her house.

5. He ran to school and was out of _____.

6. He could barely _____.

7. He looked down and his shoelace was

_____.

8. He hoped he wouldn't _____ his shoe.

9. He loudly asked a question when he was

supposed to be _____.

10. Poor Dan! He had _____ a day!

Write Your Own

WRITE

D *Use the words in ( ) to write sentences about a bad day you had. Use a dictionary if you are not sure of the meaning of the words. The first one is done for you.*

1. (peace, piece) *I ate a piece of toast on my way to school. I had no peace and quiet at home because my baby sister was not behaving.*

2. (passed, past) _____

_____

3. (missed, mist) _____

_____

4. (loose, lose) _____

_____

5. (breath, breathe) _____

_____

6. (quiet, quite) _____

_____

If you were speaking to someone about your bad day, it would be acceptable to use expressions such as bummer *or* yikes. *However, you have probably written your sentences as though for a more formal occasion. In more formal writing, you would avoid using such language.*

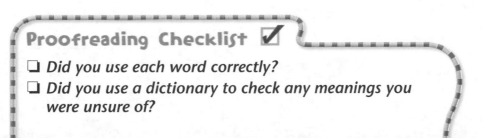

Proofreading Checklist ✔

❑ *Did you use each word correctly?*
❑ *Did you use a dictionary to check any meanings you were unsure of?*

Writing Sentences Correctly (pp. 188–191) *Write the correct end mark to end each sentence. Then write **statement, question, command,** or **exclamation** to tell what kind of sentence it is.*

1. What is your hobby ____   _____

2. Come with me to the hobby show ____   _____

3. What a great hobby this is ____   _____

Capitalizing Proper Nouns (pp. 192–195) *Read each sentence. Write each proper noun correctly.*

4. I visited san antonio.   _____

5. My cousin vicki herbert lives there.   _____

6. She painted a picture of the statue of liberty.   _____

Abbreviations (pp. 196–199) *Write the abbreviation for each day, month, and name correctly.*

7. tues   _____

8. sept   _____

9. ms Dina a Banks   _____

Book Titles (pp. 200–203) *Write each book title correctly.*

10. Coin collecting for Everyone   _____

11. a World Of Stamps   _____

12. How to find Fossils   _____

Commas (pp. 204–207) *Add commas to separate the words in a series.*

13. Dan collects stamps coins and fossils.

14. Sewing weaving and knitting are also hobbies.

15. Susan trades cards comics and stamps.

Parts of a Letter (pp. 208–211) *Write each letter part correctly.*

16. dear Laura _____

17. your friend _____

18. Billings MT 59102 _____

Quotations (pp. 212–215) *Add the missing commas and quotation marks to show each speaker's words.*

19. Carla said I like hobbies because they're fun.

20. Mike added Hobbies are also a good way to learn.

21. Jamal said Hobbies help me make friends.

Spelling Rules (pp. 216–219), **Words Often Misspelled** (pp. 220–223), **Words Often Confused** (pp. 224–227)
In item 22, circle the correct spelling of each word in ( ). In items 23–24, circle the words that correctly complete each sentence.

22. I (tried, tryed) two (kniting, knitting) lessons last week.

23. (Their, There) are (you're, your) wool socks.

24. I have (peace, piece) and (quiet, quite) when I knit.

DIRECTIONS *Fill in the circle next to the sentence that shows the correct use of commas, capital letters, end marks, spelling rules, and quotation marks.*

1. ○ The Echo Point Library is my favorite place?

   ○ You're sure to find great books, magazines, and comics there.

   ○ Its on Jackson road.

   ○ Why do I like the library!

2. ○ Ms Edith m. Foster is the children's librarian.

   ○ She can find books by title author and subject.

   ○ I really like the giant Globe.

   ○ What a wonderful book I have!

3. ○ I read short stories, poems, and picture books.

   ○ I borrowed <u>Ben And Me</u>.

   ○ I got <u>Today was A Terrible Day</u>.

   ○ <u>Collecting Coins</u> was good

4. ○ Mom gave me a wink, a smile, and a hug.

   ○ My mom asks, "why do you like the library so much?"

   ○ I tell her I loose myself in the stacks of books.

   ○ I add, "I want to read every book in the library"

5. ○ One section has almanacs encyclopedias, and atlases.

   ○ Annother room has newspapers, magazines, and journals.

   ○ I like novels, and short stories?

   ○ I also like books about real people, places, and events.

6. ○ The library is open from mon. to sat.

   ○ I can get there by car, bus, or bike.

   ○ I can also walk down Maple avenue.

   ○ I read books in Echo lake Park.

7. ○ Another librarian is Mr. Ed I Tarn.

   ○ He heard me read some poems stories and jokes.

   ○ He said, "you're our best reader."

   ○ I replied, "I can't stop reading!"

8. ○ Do I want to become a librarian when I grow up.

   ○ I thought about that this weak.

   ○ The library is the place I love most.

   ○ I want to work in a Library.

DIRECTIONS *Read the letter, and look carefully at each underlined port. Fill in the circle next to the answer choice that shows the correct use of commas, capital letters, end marks, and quotation marks. If the underlined part is already correct, fill in the circle for "Correct as is."*

99 Maple Avenue
Echo Point, IL 60544
<u>may 11 2013</u>
(9)

<u>dear ms. Hill</u>
(10)

    I am sorry to hear that the library may close on <u>mondays tuesdays and</u>
(11)

<u>fridays.</u> Many people use the library <u>daily? please</u> do not cut the days.
(11)   (12)

    My mother and I just heard about the plan to close. I <u>said, "people</u>
(13)

<u>should write</u> to the head of the library." Here is your first letter!
(13)

Sincerely <u>yours,</u>
(14)

Sal Cucio

9. ○ May 11 2013
    ○ May, 11 2013
    ◔ May 11, 2013
    ○ Correct as is

10. ○ dear Ms Hill
    ○ Dear Ms Hill,
    ○ Dear Ms. Hill,
    ○ Correct as is

11. ○ Mondays, Tuesdays, and Fridays
    ○ mondays, tuesdays and, fridays
    ○ Mondays Tuesdays and Fridays
    ○ Correct as is

12. ○ daily? Please
    ○ daily. Please
    ○ daily! please
    ○ Correct as is

13. ○ said, "People should write
    ○ said "People should write
    ○ said "people should write
    ○ Correct as is

14. ○ Sincerely yours
    ○ sincerely yours,
    ○ Sincerely Yours,
    ○ Correct as is

INDEX

A

A, an, the, 124–127
in book titles, 200
with nouns, 124, 126

Abbreviations, 196–199
and capitalization in, 196, 198
defined, 196
and periods in, 196, 198

Abstract nouns, 44–47

Action verbs, 72–75
defined, 72, 74
and object pronouns, 164, 166, 168

Addresses, abbreviations in letter
headings, 208

Adjectives, 120–123. See also *A, an, the;*
More, most
combining sentences with, 123
in comparisons, 128–131, 132–135,
136–139
defined, 120, 122
with nouns, 120, 128, 130, 136, 138
spelling rules for, 128, 130

Adverbs, 140–143
comparing with, 144–147
defined, 140, 142
spelling with *-ly*, 140
and verbs, 140

Agreement
pronoun-verb, 160–163
subject-helping verb, 100, 102
subject-linking verb, 92, 94
subject-verb, 76, 78, 80, 82, 92, 94, 100,
102, 160

And

in book titles, 200
to combine sentences with, 28, 30, 55,
75, 207
in compound sentences, 28, 30
correcting run-on sentences, 36, 38

Antecedents. *See* Pronouns and
antecedent agreement

Apostrophes
in contractions, 112, 114, 180, 182
in possessive nouns, 64

Articles. See *A, an, the*

Audience, 107, 115, 211, 215, 223

B

Be
in contractions, 112, 180
as linking verb, 92, 94, 180

Book titles. See *A, an, the,* in book titles;
And, in book titles; Capitalization, in
book titles; Italics, in book titles

But

in compound sentences, 28, 30
correcting run-on sentences, 32, 34

C

Capitalization, 188–191
in abbreviations, 196, 198
in book titles, 200, 202
in letters, 208, 210
of pronoun *I*, 156, 158
of proper nouns, 48, 50, 192–195
in quotations, 212, 214
and run-on sentences, 36
in sentences, 8, 10, 12, 16, 188, 190

Closings. *See* Letters, parts of

HOW TO USE PROOFREADING MARKS

The following paragraph illustrates all of the proofreading marks shown in the chart.

My family hiked the appalachian Trail last year. The trail runs for 2174 miles from Georgia to Maine. We started at the beginning of the Trail and hikeed up to Springer Mountain. We climbed up rocky ground and stone steps. When we got to the top, we could see for miles What a great day we had!

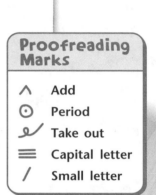

Proofreading Marks

∧	Add
⊙	Period
ℓ	Take out
≡	Capital letter
/	Small letter